A
Hampshire
Christmas

A
Hampshire
Christmas

Compiled by Sara Tiller

ALAN SUTTON

First published in the United Kingdom in 1992 by
Alan Sutton Publishing Ltd · Phoenix Mill · Far Thrupp
Stroud · Gloucestershire

First published in the United States of America in 1992 by
Alan Sutton Publishing Inc · Wolfeboro Falls
NH 03896–0848

British Library Cataloguing in Publication Data

Hampshire Christmas
I. Tiller, Sara
820.8033
ISBN 0-7509-0103-9

Library of Congress Cataloging in Publication Data
applied for

Cover illustration: Woodcutters on a winter path
*by P. Hilliot. Photograph: Joseph Mensing Gallery, courtesy of
The Bridgeman Art Library.*

Title page: The conversion of Scrooge

Typesetting and origination by
Alan Sutton Publishing Limited.
Printed in Great Britain by
The Bath Press, Bath, Avon.

Contents

A Hampshire Christmas

from

A Christmas Carol

CHARLES DICKENS

*'Bah, humbug' is how Scrooge, undoubtedly English
literature's most important Christmas character, reacts to the
coming of the festive season. A sentiment, quite probably, shared
by many modern-day Scrooges.*

*Not however a sentiment shared by Charles Dickens, author
of* A Christmas Carol, *who engineers Scrooge's conversion from
misanthropic miser to joyous philanthropist, as a lasting lesson
of Christmas charity.*

*Although Dickens spent much of his life, including his
childhood years, in London, he was born in Portsmouth, the son
of a Navy pay office clerk. Perhaps it was his father's financial
ineptitude and the hardship that his spell in a debtors' prison
caused his young family that led Dickens the younger to commit
his life to the exposure of social injustice, of which*
A Christmas Carol *is just one example.*

Once upon a time – of all the good days in the year, on
Christmas Eve – old Scrooge sat busy in his counting-house.

1

It was cold, bleak, biting weather: foggy withal: and he could hear the people in the court outside, go wheezing up and down, beating their hands upon their breasts, and stamping their feet upon the pavement stones to warm them. The city clocks had only just gone three, but it was quite dark already – it had not been light all day – and candles were flaring in the windows of the neighbouring offices, like ruddy smears upon the palpable brown air. The fog came pouring in at every chink and keyhole, and was so dense without, that although the court was of the narrowest, the houses opposite were mere phantoms. To see the dingy cloud come drooping down, obscuring everything, one might have thought that Nature lived hard by, and was brewing on a large scale.

The door of Scrooge's counting-house was open that he might keep his eye upon his clerk, who in a dismal little cell beyond, a sort of tank, was copying letters. Scrooge had a small fire, but the clerk's fire was so very much smaller that it looked like one coal. But he couldn't replenish it, for Scrooge kept the coal-box in his own room; and so surely as the clerk came in with the shovel, the master predicted that it would be necessary for them to part. Wherefore the clerk put on his white comforter, and tried to warm himself at the candle; in which effort, not being a man of a strong imagination, he failed.

'A merry Christmas, uncle! God save you!' cried a cheerful voice. It was the voice of Scrooge's nephew, who came upon him so quickly that this was the first intimation he had of his approach.

'Bah!' said Scrooge, 'Humbug!'

He had so heated himself with rapid walking in the fog and frost, this nephew of Scrooge's, that he was all in a glow; his face was ruddy and handsome; his eyes sparkled, and his breath smoked again.

'Christmas a humbug, uncle!' said Scrooge's nephew. 'You don't mean that, I am sure?'

Charles Dickens

'I do,' said Scrooge. 'Merry Christmas! What right have you to be merry? What reason have you to be merry? You're poor enough.'

'Come, then,' returned the nephew gaily. 'What right have you to be dismal? What reason have you to be morose? You're rich enough.'

Scrooge having no better answer ready on the spur of the moment, said, 'Bah!' again; and followed it up with 'Humbug.'

'Don't be cross, uncle!' said the nephew.

'What else can I be,' returned the uncle, 'when I live in such a world of fools as this? Merry Christmas! Out upon merry Christmas! What's Christmas time to you but a time for paying bills without money; a time for finding yourself a year older, but not an hour richer; a time for balancing your books and having every item in 'em through a round dozen of months presented dead against you? If I could work my will,' said Scrooge indignantly, 'every idiot who goes about with "Merry Christmas" on his lips should be boiled with his own pudding, and buried with a stake of holly through his heart. He should!'

'Uncle!' pleaded the nephew.

'Nephew!' returned the uncle, sternly, 'keep Christmas in your own way, and let me keep it in mine.'

'Keep it!' repeated Scrooge's nephew. 'But you don't keep it.'

'Let me leave it alone, then,' said Scrooge. 'Much good may it do you! Much good it has ever done you!'

'There are many things from which I might have derived good, by which I have not profited, I dare say,' returned the nephew. 'Christmas among the rest. But I am sure I have always thought of Christmas time, when it has come round – apart from the veneration due to its sacred name and origin, if anything belonging to it can be apart from that – as a good

Dickens' birthplace

time; a kind, forgiving, charitable, pleasant time; the only time I know of, in the long calendar of the year, when men and women seem by one consent to open their shut-up hearts freely, and to think of people below them as if they really were fellow-passengers to the grave, and not another race of creatures bound on other journeys. And therefore, uncle, though it has never put a scrap of gold or silver in my pocket, I believe that it *has* done me good, and *will* do me good; and I say, God bless it!'

The clerk in the tank involuntarily applauded. Becoming immediately sensible of the impropriety, he poked the fire, and extinguished the last frail spark for ever.

'Let me hear another sound from *you*,' said Scrooge, 'and you'll keep your Christmas by losing your situation! You're quite a powerful speaker, sir,' he added, turning to his nephew. 'I wonder you don't go into Parliament.'

'Don't be angry, uncle. Come! Dine with us tomorrow.'

Scrooge said that he would see him – yes, indeed he did.

5

He went the whole length of the expression, and said that he would see him in that extremity first.

'But why?' cried Scrooge's nephew. 'Why?'

'Why did you get married?' said Scrooge.

'Because I fell in love.'

'Because you fell in love!' growled Scrooge, as if that were the only one thing in the world more ridiculous than a merry Christmas. 'Good afternoon!'

'Nay, uncle, but you never came to see me before that happened. Why give it as a reason for not coming now?'

'Good afternoon,' said Scrooge.

'I want nothing from you; I ask nothing of you; why cannot we be friends?'

'Good afternoon,' said Scrooge.

'I am sorry, with all my heart, to find you so resolute. We have never had any quarrel to which I have been a party. But I have made the trial in homage to Christmas, and I'll keep my Christmas humour to the last. So A Merry Christmas, uncle!'

'Good afternoon!' said Scrooge.

'And A Happy New Year!'

'Good afternoon!' said Scrooge.

A Hampshire Christmas

JOHN ARLOTT

Born in Basingstoke on 25 February 1914, Leslie Thomas John Arlott was the son of the assistant registrar of the town cemetery, where his family lived in the lodge. He left school at sixteen and became a clerk in the local mental hospital before joining the police force in 1934.

In 1945 he joined the BBC as a poetry producer and soon began to specialize in cricket. Despite being told by one BBC executive 'You have an interesting mind, but a vulgar voice', his rich Hampshire accent earned him the nickname 'The voice of cricket', and became associated in the minds of the nation with both the essence of cricket and those qualities of Englishness that surround it – long, sunny days by the village green, country pubs and nostalgia for golden days gone by.

As well as broadcasting for the BBC, Arlott wrote several books, four hymns, and contributed to several magazines and newspapers, among them Hampshire – the county magazine, *which, in 1966, published Arlott's memories of a Basingstoke Christmas in the 1920s.*

John Arlott, 1967 – 'Basingstoke boy'

Christmas in Basingstoke forty-five years ago is still, in my mind, a brightly lit experience – the earliest and sharpest sustained recollection I have. Yet any historian would argue that December 1921 was anything but a good time. It was a cruel period of post-war inflation: prices of everything – including the simplest necessities – were rising steeply, and taxation was still levied with war time intensity; yet wages remained at pre-war levels. The number of unemployed in Britain was

increasing to two million; the national economy tottered on the brink of bankruptcy, and the Geddes axe was to fall only a few months later.

These, though, were matters far removed from the mind of a small boy. We should, perhaps, make allowances for the extravagances of boyhood memories. But not all was – or is – exaggerated. My father was back from the War. We had never seen him since the day he walked out of the house to join the army in 1915: there was no leave for ordinary soldiers in the Eastern theatre and so limited were our shipping resources that he did not eventually reach home until late 1919, a year after the end of the war. But now, at seven years old, I had for the first time in my conscious experience, a father of my own. Now, too, there were things in the shops, and on our table, that I had never *seen* before: and we were escaping from the tiny portions of 1914-War rations. To say that anything is not so good as it was is the mark of the ultimate old age – mental old age. So, almost I had tossed away this idea of a remembered Christmas as a prejudice too illogical to inflict on readers. After all, man increases his knowledge and resources: in every field where achievement can be measured he improves steadily. Christmas 1921 could not compare with Christmas 1966 – or could it? Gradually I began to see that, for a child, that earlier Christmas time *was* brighter and more stimulating: and I began to see *why* – and how to prove it.

This view of it, though is only that of a small, rather grimy, thickset boy. After a summer of historically intense sunshine, it was a bleak winter and he wore a heavy scarf round the neck of his thick – and tight – overcoat, corduroy trousers, grey socks – of which one was usually hanging down, because he could never find both his garters in the morning – and black boots: we all wore boots. On his head was a beaver hat, worn shiny: at first it was imposed on him: but when his parents

wanted to discard it, he clung to it with all the illogical stubbornness of a child striving to make opinions for himself.

He comes down Caston's entry from Fairfields School where his father went before him – a harsh, Victorian red brick building under the narrow, dark archway, and out into the Market Place. The way home was straight ahead and, even in late October, he often made his way straight home for a taste of Christmas. First point to Christmas 1921 – it began so much earlier. Mincemeat was made in October: currants were washed, raisins (seedless raisins lay still in the future) were stoned (and surreptitiously eaten) and candied peel – the huge rinds, red, yellow and green, with the wells of white melted sugar deep in the centre – chopped and chewed. Then, after the mincemeat, the Christmas pudding, made in time to 'improve' before Christmas and to allow for a 'taster' at the first Sunday dinner of December. Perhaps, too, there were paper chains to make: but most of ours were 'shop' ones – so elaborate that I fancy they were pre-1914 war – taken down every Twelfth Night, folded like concertinas and put away until the next Christmas. Certainly the main ones must have lasted us twenty years.

After these distant approaches, the town Christmas began. So turn left, along Winchester Street. Street lighting had not then reached the present uniformity which sheds a cool, even clarity everywhere. At some points the gaslights were massed so that they flowered in a huge yellow glory – nothing in any modern shopping centre stands out, or conveys such an outstanding impression of splendour as Lanhams' windows used to do at Christmas in Basingstoke, forty-odd years ago. The light ran in long, shimmering lines across the wet-black tarmac of the road, so that it was a compulsive adventure to walk along them and a kind of magic to find that, though they still ran ahead whenever we turned round, the glowing line we had already trodden had disappeared in darkness.

We would hurry disdainfully past their first windows – of curtain-material, cushions, linen and women's clothing – to the centre, where the toys were. The windows led in bright lanes to the shop doorways, and their depths made havens of warmth and shelter from the sleety evening. There was any amount of cotton-wool-snow, sprinkled with glittering white metal filings and dotted with tiny figures of Father Christmas. There was a *real* Father Christmas inside but we knew him puncturingly as 'only old Fred from along May Street' – and expensive at that. The main attraction in that year of post-war revelation was a clockwork train, running round its rails, over points, past a signal and through a station. As it disappeared beyond the window on every fourth circuit, its return was delayed while some bored, underpaid assistant wound it up: but we were not impatient. No real train was ever awaited by its passengers with more affection than that jerky, dark-green engine with its four wobbly carriages and guard's van.

At the last of the toy windows – to be saved until the end and eyed with something near reverence, far beyond hope – appeared a bicycle – not just an ordinary bicycle but a *boy's* bicycle – small, all shining and black, and with a pump and saddle-bag – 'The Bike'. We knew every angle and item of it; the line of the handlebars, the shape of the saddle: we used to stare at it, speechless. We knew the boy who got it for Christmas. We had never liked him before: we liked him less afterwards. Some 'sucked up' and begged a ride: but most stood aloof in their fierce envy: and when he fell off and cut both his knees open, no one was really sorry. It sometimes seems to me that, throughout his schooldays, he never recovered, in the esteem of his fellows, from possessing that bike.

Every item in the window, however, was a matter for criticism – of its originality and value – in conferences which might often go on for an hour or more. There was only one

cloud on that gaslit horizon. A shop-walker, with a face like weathered chalk, dressed imposingly in tail coat and striped trousers, watched us with an unwinking expression of distaste. We had long established our limits with him. So long as we were not abusive, destructive nor unduly noisy we might remain potential customers, but the urge to drive our shabby gang away from his smart window was never far behind his cold fishy eyes.

When we did leave Lanhams, there was plenty more to be seen – further credit point to 1921 – for the goods in the shops were then by no means so uniform as now. Lanhams were only the high peak. Countless small manufacturers – if even that is not a grandiose term for them – produced articles which their representative sold to a single shop in the town. No two Christmas shop windows were quite the same. We might move on to the electrician's shop – very *modern* – where, at the time, they were showing the first generally marketed electric torches. Flat, rectangular, with mock-leather coverings of various colours, they cost sixpence: and every one of us wanted one. They were an ambition not merely for the searching ray to be flicked on at will through the imposingly thick bull's eye lens, but for the battery – with one short arm and one long – which the brave tested with their tongues – the saltier it tasted the stronger it was. So our drawn-out crocodile progressed, mazily and draggingly.

It was possible to be unwittingly, but extremely, late home for the shops remained open later as Christmas approached until, for the last two or three days to Christmas Eve, the grocers worked until ten, eleven and even twelve o'clock, measuring, weighing, bagging and parcelling their endless orders. No pound of butter but must be cut off, weighed, spanked expertly between the decorated pats, and wrapped in grease-proof paper. No currants, sultanas, raisins, peel or sugar but must be shovelled out in the semi-circular, tin scoop, into the

thick blue paper bag, tossed on the scales and closed in neat triangular turns at the top: every half pound of tea was packed into lead foil bags; every rasher laboriously cut and wrapped. The butchers, greengrocers and bakers, too, worked late: and away in the remote corners of the town, faded outfitters' shops, their windows lit by a single gas mantle in a half-frosted globe, displayed their gloves and ties until an hour when few were left to look at them.

Shops then were more colourful. Less hygienic, perhaps, but they showed their goods – often sprawling far across the pavement – in vast profusion. The butchers hung their shop fronts with poultry, carcases and evergreens, and crammed their windows with pies, ox-tongues, bladders of lard, pigs'-heads-with-lemons-in-their-mouths and mighty joints so

An old-established butchers shop, Woolston, in the days when 'Pick-of-the-Market' steak was 6d a pound

prodigally that it was a wonder their assistants found time to display them all and put them away in the same day.

Wilkinson, at the fruit and flower shop in New Street, was reckoned the finest window-dresser in the town: (it is intriguing to wonder where he might have gone and done in these days) and his windows were always exciting, but especially at Christmas time. He could arrange fruit – particularly the most highly polished apples I have ever seen – with flowers – and vegetables, like celery, which he could make *look* like a flower – in such patterns that his window was a picture to arrest even the eyes of toy-obsessed schoolboys.

Again, Christmas shop *smells* were more vivid forty-five years ago. It is doubtful if there was a single refrigerator in all Basingstoke and some of the odours from frozen vegetables or sheerly rotten food were utterly offensive. But a grocer's shop *smelt* of grocery – his goods were not tucked mutely away in cellophane wrapping, but displayed boldly, to be seen – and smelt – in the large. He sold cheese and you could smell it. Gorgonzola was a special Christmas item – and it *was* gorgonzola, not Danish blue – and not a grocer but was ready with his joke about it 'talking'. An assistant would turn and pull open a drawer and the smell of cinammon, or nutmeg, ginger or cardamom, cloves or mace, allspice or carraway floated out into the medley of the air. The high, brassy coffee-mill threw out its working smell far across the street; yellow and carbolic soap formed a stern background and the gentle sugars of the dried fruit were clear to the sweet-toothed young. Dates and figs – new after the war – appeared in heavily squashed mystery, their novelty and sweetness over-riding any suggestion of nausea at the stories that the Arabs trod them into the boxes with their bare feet.

Bakers in those days *baked*: they did not merely sell goods cooked a day – and forty miles – away. The shop was full of the warm smell of new bread, soft as foam and irresistible to

the picking fingers of boyhood. The reek of doughnut fat, the deep richness of baking cakes – especially the fruity cakes, almond paste and sugar icing of Christmas – all made the shop – and the street outside – an aromatic excitement.

The dairy, with its huge green-and-white crocks, painted with flowers and country scenes, had a positive, fresh – almost frosty – smell of new milk, with just a salty hint of butter. The corn-merchant's, low-ceilinged and dark, breathed its earthy vapours out into the nostrils of the passer-by. All this was normal, but heightened at Christmas time by profusion, additions and the strange pockets of warmth which welled up from back rooms fired far into the night for the comfort of late workers and the preparation of all kinds of confections.

Perhaps there has been a change in printing methods – or materials – but the booksellers – Durrants in Winton Square – did not merely mount a display of vast extent in their improbably deep shop, but the entire place smelt, as no bookshop ever does today, of *books* – the smell, I suppose was compounded of fresh, cut paper, binder's glue and printer's ink, but I have never encountered it in such intensity since those days.

Even the familiar sweetshops varied the all-the-year-round aniseed balls, sherbet suckers, sherbet dabs, everlasting balls, fruit toffee, gob-stoppers, sweet-cigarettes, liquorice strips and the more refined almond drops and hazel fondants with chocolate 'gift boxes', Christmas crackers and crystallized fruits – and all their scents merged in a juvenile incense of heavenly sickliness.

The market went on late on Saturdays and Wednesdays before Christmas, the naphtha lamps hissed and whipped their smoke-capped flames in lurid shapes across the winter night and 'The Orange King', 'The China King', 'The Chocolate King' and 'The Potato King' hollered themselves hoarse and their goods, spilled by high-speed hurling into bags, rolled and shivered across the ground.

Above all, the streets were noisily intimate. *Almost* everyone knew *almost* everyone else and, if the traffic was too heavy for them to cross the road, one would hail another with enquiries about families and good wishes across twenty feet that separated them. Traffic was far removed from the modern uniform burble of motor cars. There were few cars; those that were to be seen banged, popped and roared alarmingly and their drivers sounded their horns as much in high spirits as warning. Horses and traps or carts were in the majority, the iron tyres gritting harshly on the grey chips spread over the winter roads: the hooves thumped or crackled according to the quality or temper of the horses and, as some small boy hung on the tail board for a free ride behind a wagon, the less fortunate would cry 'Whip behind, mister' and then you would hear the peremptory snap of the long thong. Road speeds were low and boys, and the more nimble of their elders, scuttled in urgent zig-zags between the vehicles: and bicycles curved, at all kinds of speeds, in and out of everything.

Even *domestic* noises were louder – there was no radio, no television, no talkies. In the cinema the orchestra or the single piano thundered at the ears. In houses, voices which would have filled an opera house – in volume if not in quality – rattled the walls of small front-rooms in song. Barely a house but had its piano or harmonium, and it would be an odd Christmas party if the guests did not bring their own instruments to be forced into a unison which would surprise the musical purists.

At home, too, the intensity gradually mounted along the last week to the Day – God of bile, gastritis and ulcers, what quantities we ate. The belly-pork was already in brine to be cooked and rolled and tied with string for cold breakfasts. The pork was cooking, redolent for the deeply jellied pie with the cut-out pastry flowers on top. It took two to lift the big

flagstone we used to press the tongue; and the cooking of the mince pies was an occasion of bare-faced theft and rapped fingers.

It was almost upon us. Griffin the butcher's traps, with their high-stepping ponies, moved through the streets on their delivery rounds, more arrogantly, at increasing pace and later into the evening. The postmen seemed to be delivering from morning to night.

I still retain a picture in mind, a single vignette. A tiny flurry of snow, lit yellow by a street gas-lamp and an old lady with a black bonnet, short coat and long black skirt pausing in the moment before she crossed the road, a bundle of firewood under one arm, two bottles under the other: a coal cart ground slowly by, the coalman, a sprig of mistletoe in his hat leant boozily towards her – 'Got a kiss for us Meg?' – 'Wash yer old face first' she shouted and went cackling on her way. If a child's eyes magnified it all, there was, in terms of sensory stimulus, more to be magnified – and it stood out more sharply against the background of a general simplicity which had not yet gone down before sophistication.

Some inbuilt emotional control must have adjusted the almost unbearable excitement so that it reached its just-containable peak by bed-time on Christmas Eve, and allowed it to subside to the brink of sleep an hour before the presents were put softly beside the bed. There they were in the morning – not morning, really – still night – explored first with groping hand and then! look at the rest with *my own* electric torch – at all the impossible presents – how did they *know*? Open-mouthed through all those weeks to that final heady morning – such a morning as has left many of us striving ever since, through the dim, almost perverse, inarticulate failure of children, to utter the adequate 'thank you' for the actuality – and the recollection – of it.

from

Nothing to Steal

NANCY SHARMAN

*Nancy Sharman was born and brought up in Northam, one
of the notorious slum areas of Southampton.*

*As the title of her book suggests, her childhood was spent in
poverty, but however spartan her Christmas may sound to the
modern reader, there are many who will share the author's
obvious nostalgia for a time when Christmas was a far simpler
festival.*

Christmas was a lovely time for us children. I soon got on the
bandwagon of carol-singing for money. Ken and I would go
out together but not often with Dorothy as she was such a
delicate child and very chesty. After each night's carol
singing, we would get home and eagerly count our takings;
we got between two and three shillings on our best night.
Takings varied from night to night, however; we always did
better in the poorer areas than we did in the so-called posh
ones. With our takings we could buy Mum and Uncle Joe a
little present and, of course, get something for each other and
Dorothy. On Christmas Eve, we hung our socks on the end of
the bed and no modern child with all the expensive gifts of
today could have appreciated its contents more than we did.
Each sock would contain an orange, an apple, some nuts and a

Northam High Street in flood

small present. Mum paid tuppence or thruppence every week to a toy-and-bicycle shop on the corner; she always made sure that we each had some present for Christmas. Sometimes we had rabbit for Christmas dinner and once we had a chicken that Uncle Joe won in a draw. It was lovely for us to have Mum home for a whole day.

Food Glorious Food

IRENE SOPER

As Christmas is a busy time in everyone's kitchen Irene Soper
devotes a whole chapter in her book New Forest Cookery *to*
local Christmas recipes, guiding the reader through every stage
of the festive season.

November the twenty-sixth really sees the start of the
preparations for Christmas in the New Forest. For that is the
traditional date on which the Gypsies are allowed to start
picking holly to sell at local markets and to make wreaths.
Already they have filled their sacks with moss gathered from
the boggy paths on the side of the hill above Abbots Well.
This moss is used in the foundations of wreaths. One old
Gypsy lady living in the village can always be seen at that
time of year colourfully dressed in a long skirt, short coat
with flowered apron and headscarf, pushing a pram overflow-
ing with holly towards the town.

Our small local Forest town Fordingbridge is a throng of
activity as the festive season progresses. Outside the butchers
shop hang rows of hares, pheasants and turkeys. Lighted
Christmas trees shine above every shop and in the square
people gather to sing traditional carols around a bigger lit
tree. Back in the village the carol singers find their way along
the dark lanes by the light of a lantern on a long pole. At one
time carol singers on Christmas Eve were given a warming
spiced drink. The Christmas Wassail Bowl was usually

New Forest gypsies. On 26 November gypsies are traditionally
allowed to start picking holly

composed of a strong ale, the froth of roasted apples, cloves,
cinnamon, and a grate of nutmeg, ginger and brown sugar.

Through the open doorway of the village church comes the
sound of more carols sung this time to the accompaniment of
the local silver band. Approaching the church, our pathway is
gilded by the glowing colours of a stained glass window.

Inside a huge Christmas tree stands shining with coloured
lights and cascades of gold and silver tinsel. Every seat is
filled and after the service coffee and sandwiches are served in
the adjacent hall where everyone can meet and discuss the
coming festive season.

On Christmas Eve the kitchen is a very busy place.
Although the cake and puddings have been made for several

weeks there are still the mince pies to make, the chestnut stuffing to mix, vegetables to prepare, the trifle to make and the cake to decorate.

CHRISTMAS CAKE

Ten ounces of plain flour, pinch of salt, one level teaspoonful of mixed spice, half a level teasponful of grated nutmeg, four ounces of glace cherries, twelve ounces of seedless raisins, twelve ounces of sultanas, eight ounces of currants, eight ounces of butter, eight ounces of soft brown sugar, four eggs, two tablespoonfuls of sherry, two ounces of whole almonds, one ounce of crystallized ginger, one heaped teaspoonful of grated lemon rind, two ounces of mixed peel, chopped.

Grease a round eight inch deep cake tin. Line with two layers of greased greaseproof paper. Tie a double band of brown paper round the outside of the tin.

Pre-heat oven to 350°F and reduce to 300°F after fifteen minutes.

Sift flour, salt, spice, and nutmeg into a bowl. Wash and dry the cherries. Chop fairly finely. Clean the raisins, sultanas and currants by putting them in a sieve with a little extra flour. Rub well until all the flour falls through the sieve, discard flour. Cream butter and brown sugar in a bowl until smooth and fluffy. Beat eggs together in a basin. Gradually beat eggs into the creamed mixture. Stir in the sherry. Put almonds into a small pan of water and bring to the boil. Drain and skin. Cut the nuts finely. Chop the ginger. Stir together ginger, almonds, cleaned fruit, cherries, lemon rind and peel. Stir fruit and nuts mixture into the sifted flour, and gradually fold into creamed mixture.

Put into prepared tin, smooth the top and make a well in centre. Cook on lower shelf of the oven for four hours. When cake is quite cold, and it should be left to cool for twelve

hours, wrap in a clean cloth, then in greaseproof paper, until ready to ice.

It was once the custom in the old farmhouses to serve a dish called Frumenty for breakfast at Christmas-time.

FRUMENTY

One dish of crushed whole wheat, sugar, spice, and raisins and skimmed new milk, simmered in a jar in the oven, or at the back of the stove overnight. It can be eaten hot or cold.

On the farmsteads it is possible a fat capon was served for Christmas dinner, and most likely in some more remote cottages a joint of venison would grace the table at the Festive season.

After a traditional Christmas lunch in the middle of the day only a light tea was wanted. This was usually eaten around the open fire, and was probably just a sweet.

CHRISTMAS FIRESIDE WASSAIL BOWL
(A delicious sweet)

Half a pound of macaroons, six penny sponge cakes (trifle sponges), one ounce of powdered sugar, raisin wine, two ounces of raisins and two pints of custard.

Crumble the macaroons and sponge cakes into a large glass dish, mix with the sugar and raisins, and saturate them thoroughly with the wine. Prepare the custard and pour over the whole of the above, stirring gently to mix perfectly. After it is cold, garnish the surface, with blanched sweet almonds and glace cherries, and serve from the dish.

On Boxing Morning the New Forest pony races are held. The start is kept secret until just before-hand, only the finish is known. This is to ensure that no one can ride the course in advance. Ponies and riders gallop across the Forest and come in covered with mud but enjoying every minute of it. Watching these races can be a very chilly occupation for the spectator; we traditionally take a flask of ginger wine to keep out the cold.

OLD RECEIPE FOR GINGER WINE

For the wine, use *three pounds of sugar, one lemon, three ounces of root ginger well bruised, and half a pound of stoned raisins, to the gallon of water. A quarter of a pint of brandy* may be added when the wine is finished.

Boil all the ingredients together for one hour, skimming carefully. When the liquor is quite clear, strain it into a jar or tub, and when it is cool add a *tablespoonful of dry yeast*. Stir this mixture everyday for a fortnight while adding *another half pound of raisins*. At the end of that time, strain the wine into a cask, add the brandy, bottle and cork down when all hissing has ceased. It will be ready in a few weeks, but will improve if kept.

Following a morning of standing around a good sharp walk may be needed in the afternoon to stimulate the circulation! I recall one Boxing Day walk with my husband after a heavy fall of snow. We walked across the Forest to a small wooded enclosure where we knew there was a badger sett. We found distinctive badger prints in the snow around the holes where they had come out the previous night to forage. The light was fading as we turned for home and in the holly trees silhouetted against the cold sky were redwings and fieldfare feeding on the berries.

New Forest in winter

We reached our cottage at dusk, the air chill with frost, but through the window we could see the cheering sight of the lighted Christmas tree and a blazing log fire. Inside my mother had tea ready, hot mince pies, and a bowl of trifle in the centre of the table.

MINCEMEAT

One pound of cooking apples, one pound of currants, one pound of sultanas, one pound of raisins, one pound of chopped or shredded suet, one pound of soft brown sugar, quarter of a pound of minced candied peel, four ounces of finely minced blanched almonds, quarter of a level teaspoonful of mixed spice, half a level teasponful of grated nutmeg, half a lemon, one large wineglass full of brandy.

Wash and dry the fruit, cut the raisins into quarters, roughly chop the sultanas, and leave the currants whole. Peel, core and chop the apples. Mix all the ingredients together with the brandy and the strained juice and grated rind of the half lemon. Put into a large wide mouthed jar, put a piece of greaseproof paper, cut to fit over the mincemeat and dipped in brandy, over the top. Seal the jar with two or three thicknesses of greaseproof paper and store the jar in a very cool, dry place.

MINCE PIES

Butter some tin pattypans well, and line them evenly with *fine puff paste rolled thin; fill them with mincemeat,* moisten the edges of the covers, which should be nearly a quarter of an inch thick, close the pies carefully, trim off the superfluous paste, make a small aperture in the centre of the crust with the point of a knife, sugar the pies or not, at pleasure, and bake them half an hour in a well-heated but not too hot oven: lay a paper over them when they are partially done, should they appear likely to take too much colour.

TRIFLE

Line the bottom of a glass trifle dish with *sponge cakes stuck with blanched almonds; moisten with sweet wine, or with sherry and sugar.* Over these lay *a dozen ratafias.* Between these put *thin slices of citron and orange peel,* and put over these pieces of *apricot and raspberry jam with currant jelly.* Pour over *a few spoonfuls of the liquor.* The next layer should consist of *tartlet cream* about an inch thick, over which grate *some nutmeg and sprinkle a little powdered cinnamon* together with *a small quantity of lemon peel and some powdered loaf sugar.* Lastly top *with whipped cream* as much as the dish will contain. To decorate strew various coloured comfits over the cream.

The tartlet cream may be made as follows: Mix together *half a pint of cream* and *the same quantity of milk*; put into it *a piece of fresh lemon peel or Seville orange peel and a little cinnamon, and sweeten with loaf sugar.* Let these ingredients boil for about ten minutes. Have ready prepared in another pan *the yolks of six eggs* well beaten *with a heaped teaspoonful of fine flour*; to these gradually strain ingredients, and then whisk together over a gentle fire (burner) that they may acquire the proper consistency without curdling.

It was once the custom to celebrate the 'Feast Of The Stars' by holding a 'Twelfth Night' party. A special cake was baked for the occasion very rich and spicy. It was iced with a blue coloured icing to represent the sky and decorated with silver stars and twelve candles.

TWELFTH NIGHT CAKE

Eight ounces of flour, four eggs, eight ounces of sugar, eight ounces of butter, one level dessertspoon of mixed spice, six ounces of currants, eight ounces of sultanas, two ounces of candied peel, two ounces of glace cherries and a little milk to mix.

Grease a cake tin and line with paper. Prepare the dry ingredients. Cream the butter and sugar together, beat in each egg separately, stir in the sieved flour and spice, fruit, etc., alternately with the milk, adding a little of each at a time.

Blend all the ingredients together, put into a prepared tin, and bake in a moderate oven of about 350°F for two hours. When cold, ice with pale blue icing and decorate as suggested.

Some Ghosts of Christmas Past . . .

JOAN GRIGSBY

*For six consecutive years, five of them during the Second
World War, Hampshire born Joan Grigsby was posted overseas
with her husband. This meant Christmas away from home and
Joan confessed she found herself longing for 'the English
countryside in winter, a Christmas complete with snow, log
fires, a Christmas tree and, yes – even cold feet'.*

*But, as Joan discovered one Christmas Day in Ceylon,
however far from home you are, there is no getting away from
your Hampshire roots.*

In order to comfort me in my exile and create a picture of the
England I liked to remember, I had taken with me a number
of books. To these I added more and more as the all too rare
consignments arrived from England to the bookshops in
whichever part of the Far or Middle East we had reached at
the time. Looking at them now, as many of them stand in
faded, slightly battered ranks on my bookshelves, it seems a
curious coincidence to discover that most of those which tell
of Christmas at home are by writers who have some connection, however tenuous, with our own county, even though the
scenes they describe are not necessarily Hampshire scenes.

'"Fine weather for those who is well wrapped up" said the Polar bear as he practised his skating.' Sam Weller was awakening Mr Pickwick on Christmas morning, and lying in bed under my mosquito net I chuckled as I had done many times before. Somewhere along the line the first volume of my Oxford Pocket edition of *The Pickwick Papers* had got lost and Vol. II began with Christmas at Dingley Dell. To be fair, Charles Dickens, born (as I was myself), in Portsmouth, spent only the first two years of his life there, so despite the enjoyment that Pickwick and his friends always gave me, one could not honestly claim either him or them as Hampshire characters. But that Christmas Day in Ceylon was to bring an experience which went so deep into our roots in Hampshire that I have never quite forgotten it.

We were sitting at dinner in the garden of The Residency at Galle, an attractive old Dutch–Portuguese town in the south-west of the island, not far from where, on a lake in the middle of what was virtually jungle, our flying boats had found a temporary resting place. It was very hot; from the native village below we could just hear the persistent throb of drums, and the candles on the table barely flickered.

Christmas pudding seemed a most unseasonable dish, but tradition had to be observed and we battled on. We knew that our host and his sister came from the west country so we were rather surprised when, in the course of conversation which had inevitably strayed to stories of Christmas at home, he announced that way back his family had been settled in Hampshire. 'Whereabouts?' I queried. 'Mottisfont Abbey, not far from Kings Somborne.' My husband looked at him for a moment; he seemed slightly puzzled. 'That's funny,' he said, 'an ancestor of mine round about the thirteenth century founded the Abbey for his brother, who was a priest, a sort of hermit in fact. He lived in a cell in a wall and was thought to work miracles. Peter de Rivallis they called him – the hermit, not his brother – he was quite a different type. The family

were about there for some time, at Kings Somborne and Longstock and thereabouts; but then they faded out. Recusants I suppose, papists, anyway.'

Our host, who was the gentlest and most courteous of men, smiled rather apologetically. 'That would explain it,' he said; 'my family came along at the Dissolution and the Abbey was made over to them. I'm sorry.' For a moment we were all silent. The candles burned on steadily; the ghosts of over five centuries hung suspended in the hot still air, but I felt a curious tingling down my spine, a sudden quickening of the senses. It was all so far away and long ago, and here we were all discussing it as if it were yesterday. 'It's a lovely house now,' I commented, 'Rex Whistler has been painting a room there. When all this is over and you come and stay with us in the Forest, we must all go over and have a look.' And the spell was broken.

Christmastide

THOMAS HARDY

Although Thomas Hardy is perhaps more closely associated with Dorset than neighbouring Hampshire, any map of his fictitious Wessex will show that a large portion of Hampshire falls within its boundaries.

With this in mind I have no qualms about including some of Hardy's poems in this collection, despite the gloomy style of the author.

A Hampshire Christmas

The rain-shafts splintered on me
As despondently I strode;
The twilight gloomed upon me
And bleared the blank high-road.
Each bush give forth, when blown on
By gusts in shower and shower,
A sigh, as it were sown on
In handfuls by a sower.

A cheerful voice called, nigh me,
'A merry Christmas, friend!' –
There rose a figure by me,
Walking with townward trend,
A sodden tramp's, who, breaking
Into thin song, bore straight
Ahead, direction taking
Toward the Casuals' gate.

from

My Old Chap

NORMAN GOODLAND

Back in March 1950, the Southern Evening Echo
*reported that a '31-year-old farm worker with literary
ambitions, Norman Goodland, of Michelmarsh, near Romsey'
was to talk on the wireless about the relations of the farm
worker to his employer.*

*Goodland's talks took off and he was soon to become a
familiar voice to listeners of the West Home Service and
something of a local celebrity for his radio broadcasts.*

Goodland who, according to the Echo *report in 1950,
'writes in the spare time left after the needs of the farm, a wife
and two strapping young boys have been attended to' published
his first novel in 1948.*

Since then he has published many successful books including
My Old Chap, *a collection of dialect verses based on the life of
Frank West, clerk, sexton and gravedigger to the Church of
St Stephen in Baughurst.*

*The following two poems from this volume capture some
aspects of the rural Christmas enjoyed by West, also a thatcher
and a waterdiviner by trade.*

Norman Goodland, local broadcaster

Christmas Be Come

Christmas be come
Winter be 'ard.
Frost do 'ang white in leane.
Woods be all dark;
hedges leary –
Snaw d'come back agean.

Rooks d'bide whoam.
Plover d'cry.
Cows be all stood b'geate.
'ouse-mouse d'scratch –
dusk d'come down.
Flames is all blue in greate.

Kittle d'zing –
tea ben all laid;
chillern comes in vrom play.
Vixen d'scream:
owl zets in tree.
'Whit-wheet! Whit-wheet!' he d'zay!

When Christmas Passed This Way

When Christmas passed this way
we comed up to the Church.
We villed up all the pews –
we zat, we zung, we prayed.
We yeard agen the good old tale –
the Parson 'e did say:
'A stable was 'is birthplace –
and 'umble was 'is way.'
Then arterwards, 'e shook our 'ands
and wished us a good day.

Then – 'e got in 'is motor-car –
and 'e did drive away.

When Christmas passed this way
we comed down to The Bear.
We went into the bar –
we 'adn't got awver yesterday –
but still, it wouldn't be right
if we missed Fred, and Frank and they
as comed back whoam to zee us
vrom villages away.
We drank, we laughed, we zung:
'Appy Christmas!' we did zay
to them we'd pass wi' nar a word
on any other day.

Then – we got in our motor-cars –
and we did drive away.

When Christmas passed this way
we comed into the town.
We stood up by the Gents
and what we 'ad to say
was jes the seame as what was said
on any other day,
except – we said it louder –
for being Christmas Day
there were more folks to stare, and more
of we to stare at they.

Then – we got on our motor-bikes –
and we did roar away.

A Hampshire Christmas

When Christmas comed this way –
it comed that quiet, and still
you might've 'ardly noticed it:
but Bert, and Auntie May –
was here for Christmas dinner;
and arterwards did stay
to talk of Dad, and Mother,
Gert and Flo – all passed away –
and 'ow Tory sang the carols
in the years of yesterday.
Then – we did kiss each other.
'Come more often' we did zay.

Then – they got in the motor-car –
and they did drive away.

When Christmas passed this way
another crib they made.
The same old box and wooden cows
we zid last Christmas Day . . .
the seame old figures starin' stiff
at where the babe do lay. . . .
But – look'e at them chillern!
They comes – they stares – they stays.
'There's sheep in there – an 'orses –
an' that's Mary!' one d'zay!
'An' there's Shepherds luk – an' angels
an' three Wise Men to pray!'
I s'pose 'tis – sart o' – marvellous –
when you'm as young as they . . .

't wun't 'urt t' bide a bit –
avor we drives awaay . . . !

Hogmanay in Hampshire

C.W. HAWKINS

Hampshire has a number of 'military towns', whose relatively small populations are constantly swelled by the soldiers stationed in nearby barracks.

The sheer presence of large numbers of dashing young men from as far afield as northern England, Wales or Scotland has enriched the life of these Hampshire towns. For generations these soldiers have been sweethearts to the young women of Hampshire and role models for the young men.

In the following extract C.W. Hawkins recalls how the arrival of two battalions of the Royal Scots, on their way to the trenches in 1914, transformed a traditional New Year's Eve in the military town of Alton into what was, for many of the unfortunate Scotsmen, their last Hogmanay.

On the last day of November, 1914, the 11th and 12th Battalions of the Royal Scots came to the town, and were billeted in houses, halls and schools, and early in January they were replaced by the 7th Battalion the Seaforth Highlanders and the 8th Battalion Black Watch, who remained in the town until nearly the end of March. There were about 2,000 soldiers in the

town in addition to a detachment of the Hampshire Regiment, which was located in Westbrook House.

The committee formed by the Urban District Council was instrumental in establishing a canteen and recreation room in the stabling at the rear of the Pavement (now Lloyds Bank) for the Scottish troops billeted in the town during the first winter of the war.

Scottish Hogmanay was celebrated in this Hampshire market town on New Year's Eve, 1914, the following description of the event appearing in the local press:

The year 1914 closed and the year 1915 was welcomed in a unique manner. Never had Alton witnessed a Scots New Year's Eve–Hogmanay. This important function was organised by the officers and men of the Royal Scots (11th and 12th Battalions), and about 1,600 of them assembled in the great cellar at Messrs. Crowley & Co.'s brewery. The place was decorated with evergreens and flags, and an excellent four hours' concert was arranged. The memory of those present was impressed by the sight of the khaki-clad men who sang the favourite chorus 'Tipperary'. Military and civilian friends and the Alton band assisted with the programme. At midnight a fairy announced the New Year's wish 'Royal Scots. Good Luck!'. Cheers, Auld Lang Syne and the National Anthem closed the gathering. In the streets, as the soldiers dispersed, it was estimated that there were about 3,000 people (soldiers and civilians). Bagpipes were playing, and so dawned the stirring year of 1915.

Stirring indeed. Ere long numbers of these Scottish lads, who had become very popular in the town, had found their final resting places in a foreign field.

New Year's night was to remain a striking memory to me, for my mother took us down the street to witness the events. We heard the bagpipes, saw the kilted soldiers, but were disappointed because the sentries failed to challenge us.

Christmas Songs

THE GYPSIES

The gypsies of Hampshire and particularly the New Forest were traditionally smiths, musicians, hawkers, fortune tellers and horse dealers, but there are over a hundred other occupations listed by the Gypsy Lore Society.

New Forest gypsies preparing to move on, 1961

Door-to-door selling also provided an opportunity for the gypsies to peddle their hand-made wares and in the New Forest, in particular, they once collected discarded fire grates, kettles, teapots, candlesticks and any other old iron.

Always an isolated community, living close to the poverty line, their hard life is reflected in two rather bitter Christmas songs, which were sung by the gypsies as they travelled the lanes of the county.

The roads are very dirty, my shoes are very thin,
I have a little pocket to put my money in.
Your pocket full of money, your cellar full of beer,
I wish you merry Christmas and happy New Year.

The moon shone bright and the stars gave a light, a little before it was day,
The Lord our God when he died on the cross, he bade us to wait and to pray;
Wait awhile good people wait, wait and hear again,

New Forest gypsies, 1963

It may be better for your poor souls when your body lies
  under the main.
A life hath a man, it is only a span, he flourished just like a
  flower,
He's here today and tomorrow away, he's alive and he's dead in
  hour.
My curls are down and I must go, no longer can I stay here,
Lord bless you all, both great and small, and send you a
  Happy New Year.

Christmas Customs

FROM *THE COUNTY MAGAZINE*

In 1786 The County Magazine *declared itself to be*
'particularly dedicated to the inhabitants of Berkshire,
Dorsetshire, Hampshire, Somersetshire and Wiltshire'.

Inside its heavily bonded pages there was, it claimed on its
frontispiece, 'a copious section of whatever is valuable in
literature, politics and history and the greatest variety of
miscellaneous and original pieces in prose and verse.'

One such gem, which appeared in the 1788 edition, took an
interesting look at the Christmas customs of the region.

There are many good old customs appropriated to this season of the year, which, although banished by the refinement of the metropolitans, are still preserved in various parts of the country as introductive of harmless mirth, and emblematic of things almost forgotten.

On Christmas Eve it is still a custom in the North to light candles of a very uncommon size, which are called Christmas candles: to burn also a yule log, or Christmas block thus illuminating the house. The custom perhaps borrowed from the Saxons; they began their year on the eighth of the calends of January which is our Christmas Day. The night before was called by them 'the night of mothers' and was observed by them as sacred. The log, perhaps, was burned in imitation of the son's return.

The origin of Christmas-boxes is said to be this: The priests said masses for everything. If a ship went on a distant voyage, a box was fixed to the mast and consecrated to some saint. The mariners were expected to put money into this box that masses might be said for them on their return. The mass was then called Christmas; this particular box the Christmas box. Many other customs may be enumerated: the Christmas carol, Christmas pies. At the universities it is common to hang laurel in all the colleges and chapels, which when we consider that the laurel was emblematical of peace and victory, is easily explained. One of the earlier councils forbade Christians to deck their houses with bay leaves and green boughs – but there is, thank heaven, no restraint upon what leads to cheerfulness, and the careful cook may enjoy her mistletoe without fear of being disturbed by the censures of the church.

God Bless Us, Every One

CHARLES CLARK

*Born in Portsmouth, Charles Clark was brought up in
Sandringham Road in the opening years of the century.*

*Although in his introduction he says he believes Dickens was
too colourful in his description of the Cratchit family, his own
memories of an Edwardian Christmas in Portsmouth are
equally as rosy and should be enjoyed by those who remember the
Pompey of old.*

I have always felt that Charles Dickens was too colourful in
his description of the Cratchit family in the *Christmas Carol*
but considering the time at which it was written there can be
no doubt that the high spots, the low spots and the exaggera-
tions were necessary to readers whose lives were so drab that
they hung upon any words that described the luxuries they
would seldom receive and found in the descriptions of depri-
vation and misery conditions worse than their own.

Throughout it all shines that typical national asset of those
times and later, a response to anything that even resembled
humour and a sense of good fun that transcended conditions
that today would be called piteous.

It might therefore be of interest to look back upon the early

Edwardian period and recount briefly the Christmas time of a family that were possibly a little, but very little above working class average, with the ever present bogey of not being able to make ends meet in a small building business that had little ambition other than to get work, irrespective of any conscious knowledge of how to make profit to keep the men fully employed.

Dimly perhaps, I believe that my Father drew two golden sovereigns each week as his standard drawing, with a golden half sovereign extra for Christmas; against the craftsman's one and half golden sovereigns as his week's pay. Both may easily have been less at that particular time, but I cannot be too adamant as it meant so little to we children, of whom there were two boys and two girls. The season's approach was possibly heralded by the arrival of *The Yule Log*, an almost fire-coloured addition to the local 'News' containing seasonable stories, including ghostly ones for grown ups, a new or old carol, riddles and jokes and suchlike quips. Father got *The Strand Magazine* with its light green cover somewhat embellished as a compliment to the season, and possibly containing a new story of mystery and detection by Sherlock Holmes whose name was then better known among average readers than that of his creator Conan Doyle.

The making of decorative paper chains, consisting of small bundles of various coloured papers about 6" long by 1" wide, and which always contained one or two silvered ones in each batch, formed into links by pasting each one with flour paste, under supervision and help, took up an evening, and these we carefully strung across or around the walls, avoiding the gas brackets. Holly completed the decoration and mistletoe was always hung somewhere convenient for Father, to our amusements, could kiss any and every female who entered the house, and took full advantage of it – as a custom, of course!

Next came the visit to Grandpa Colligan who kept a tiny

vegetable and fruit shop at North Street, Portsea. He had always taken an ounce of 'shag' tobacco as his Christmas present, for use with his clay pipe, and we were thanked by a kiss from a prickly bearded face; a salutation that we did not really like. Our gracious Grandmother received her simple gift with due dignity.

We came away laden with apples, oranges, grapes and nuts of all kinds for which Father, now illuminated by a 2d. cigar, had paid but few shillings. The goodies were split up into three and we each carried our share, resisting the temptation to steal even one sweet 'new nut' or a luscious grape from Spain. We seldom saw fruit during normal times, except apples, and by tradition these, my Mother always said 'Were good for you!'

Carol singing, I believe, did not commence until quite close to the 25th, and then consisted mostly of grown-ups in what was possible church groups; and a few singles or couples who literally 'sang for their supper'.

There was always some minor – at least – illness among the prevailing large families at that time of year, especially among children, when clothing, heating and general conditions, even of the best were primitive compared with those of today.

If it was not a common cold it could be ear or tooth ache, mumps, tonsilitis or one of a dozen other ailments that today can be relieved by an injection or a tablet; but let us forget all about this sad side as it is the festive season; but before doing so must recount lying in bed with some indisposition in the week of Christmas.

The probably still early night was dark; the room, normally occupied by my brother and self lit by a single 'gas jet' with blue centre and yellow outer edges of flame that flickered almost nervously. In the semi-darkness there started a scratching noise (it could have been a stray mouse, they were quite common with unprotected food about, and such domestic

necessities as chicken, kept for eggs). 'Must be someone in the wardrobe' thought I. Combine this with the commencement out in the street of someone singing 'Noel' which to me was a strange and solemn dirge, and you will appreciate the near panic with which I called 'Clara, Clara, Clara' to an eleven year older cousin who was a constant help and comfort to my Mother. She climbed the stairs her voice joining those of the outside singers, came into the room, opened the doors of the wardrobe, signified that there was no one in it, shut it up and disappeared still lost in wonder at the carol; but I was satisfied. I am sure that she thought the carol wonderful.

On Christmas day we children were full of excitement and anticipation and more noisy that at any other time. There was always a good big turkey, provided by a mysterious Mr Morley, who had served my father some dirty business trick at some time or other. This is quite true, and I have wondered many times since whether he had read or seen Dickens's story, compared himself to Marley (the name similarity is significant) and appeased his conscience by sending this annual gift until he died. I met him once in my early twenties, when he called to see my father for the one and only time. He was then a very old, quiet and humbled man who greeted me silently.

To proceed. On Christmas eve after an unexpected treat of a drink of Baggs or Mumby's fizzy lemonade procured from a bottle kept full of gas by a glass marble held in place by a red rubber ring that had to be pressed in to get at the contents, we volunteered for early bed, determined in only half belief to stop awake to discover who this mysterious 'Father Christmas', who strangely ventured down the dirty chimney and left gifts for children, really was!

Having shouted our demands up the chimney for some nights in succession, these requests had gradually gone down as Mother had explained that the poor man had to come so far,

that his sleigh could only hold a limited number of things and that these must go to the poorest children first and that we, fortunate in having both father and mother, must accept what was left. This did not prevent my brother and I from hanging on each of the brass knobs at the foot of the bed the largest stocking each that we could find. Under the bed-clothes conversation on the subject gradually dwindled as anticipation, excitement and mother nature took its toll of young bodies and we were soon asleep despite all our resolves. We thought we were early awake next morning but had we observed the light coming through the window would have known that we were much later, because for us all there was no need to hurry for work or school.

Then a scramble. What had we got? It did not differ much from year to year, unless some unexpected bad debt had been paid – each an apple, an orange, one or two newly minted copper pennies, a small packet of Fry's plain chocolate, always a tiny sugar pink pig, some nuts, a few sweets done up in coloured paper, a 'bon-bon' (now called a 'cracker'), a piece of coal for next year's luck with never more than one small toy each. I remember that mine on one occasion was a then traditional pen and pencil box, cut out of the solid and carefully gouged out with a lathe, that had on its lid a picture of British soldiers, some with bandaged heads, striking down the enemy with their swords and no doubt inspired by the recent Boer war.

We must have decided, in the way of children, that old Father Christmas had done his best for us and so were content to contemplate the next excitement, that of the Christmas dinner.

This festive time was completely a family affair for most of them were of not less than six with parents, and a large proportion many more, so that two families together plus some grandparents were more than enough both for the room available, and the victuals that could be provided.

My parents always invited my Mother's youngest sister with her batch of girl children, and her husband whom I will call Uncle 'P' for the purposes of this narrative. She was of help to my Mother in the preparations. He was a carpenter and joiner by trade who looked after his family well, sometimes working for my Father, but would go off at an hour's notice, to work on any job where there was overtime. This was apparently never resented, and he would come back at intervals, possibly at the intervention of my Mother, even if someone else had to go to make room for him. Although he always wore a dreamy look, with eyes that were half closed when conversing, these light blue orbs were a feature of prominence that could not be missed. He was far from dreamy at work and his eyes always opened wider at the prospect of an hour's overtime, or a job on the side. To his credit all the family were well dressed and what my Father described as 'Pharo's lean kine', but Mother with perhaps a trifle of envy always remarked that it was a pity they did not 'put into their stomachs what they put on their backs. It would do them more good.' This holiday time was one of the few when the man of the house deemed it necessary to give a hand to his hard pressed wife, and in this my father was no exception; doing what was necessary, and further to butcher the poor turkey that had arrived complete with body contents and fully feathered.

With the arrival mid-morning of Uncle and Auntie P and family his domestic labours ceased and the two men were off for a drink or two while the women continued the preparations and pacified six or more excited small children. The very important 'Christmas puddings' had been made weeks before, when everyone had been invited to 'have a stir' for luck; and Auntie P had brought one of her own make to help out.

My Mother never failed to remonstrate the late return home of the husbands, Father full of fun as he sharpened the

carving knife, but Uncle P after a couple of drinks, looking more sleepy than usual and making almost inaudible agreements with anything that was said, even by we children.

The meal was always a full and very good one, aided of course by the traditional turkey, and we youngsters invariably ate too much, with an occasional hurried exit, accompanied by an adult. Compliments about the meal were general. I do not remember what happened for the next hour or two, but probably the youngest and the eldest at least closed their eyes for awhile; others played 'Snakes and ladders', 'Ludo', or dominoes, or maybe did a little reading. The early evening was something of a repeat of the mid-day meal, served cold and in smaller quantities, with some not wanting much but fruit and nuts, which included chestnuts cooked in a small shovel over a coal fire that blazed with extra fuel for this festive day. Father would then produce his (then) 3/6d. bottle of 'Scotch' as a special treat and the fun-sized Havana cigar. The fun began as gradually Uncle P became good temperedly voluble and melodious. He always told stories of his work, in which he was very interested, then about the family, and always ended with a description of his own father which ran something like this . . . 'My old man was one of the best dressed men in Town. Good suit, good boots, nicely coloured waistcoat, expensive hat, nice shirt and classy tie, double gold albert with a spade guinea on it in full display, gold watch in the waistcoat pocket. Not too showy – but a gold and diamond ring on each hand! Real silver band on his walking stick, and to top it all a real pearl tie pin that showed quality. Yes, that was my old man, and when he was dressed up like that I reckon he was a fifty-pound man!'

As the evening wore on and the ladies had settled down there was probably an attempt to sing a carol or two, or play, on the early Edison Bell phonograph with its brown wax cylindrical records, some tunes of which the best remembered

is 'My little gipsy sweetheart' – it always brought tears to my childish eyes. The sweet but tinny tones of the 'Musical box' provided an alternative, but the difficulty of winding and the repetition of its eight items soon caused it to be abandoned.

By this time, however, aided by a whisky or two and the unaccustomed drug of a cigar, Uncle P began to sing. His curly hair became more dishevelled with the advancing hours, his eyes looked supersize, but half closed with the cadence of the words of the song, and so he went on!

Judging the time for the departure of our visitors nicely, and it could not have been very late as they had to walk home whatever the weather, Father would pour out a last drink and then say 'Come on P let's have your favourite!' The gas jet was turned down for this performance, and we all braced ourselves for the final performance of the evening. This consisted of Uncle P's rendering of an almost tuneless dirge that I have only once since heard repeated:

I am the ghost of John James Christopher Benjamin Binns,
I've come right up out of the mist of my sins,
Old Leo is down below, I've come up for an hour or so –
Until the cock begins to crow; then fare-well,
John James Christopher Benjamin Binns, Binns, Binns!

There were no doubt other verses, and at the end of each we kids all come in with the – Binns . . . Binns . . . Binns!

This marked the end of our Christmas Day. Nobody ever said 'God bless us, every one' nor was 'Auld Lang's syne' ever voiced, but just a tired out bunch of children eager for their beds.

When this task was over my parents no doubt sat down to a $2\frac{1}{2}$d. pint bottle of Pike Spicer's light ale, as was their custom, and probably wondered what the New Year would bring. They are still remembered with a kindly affection.

from

Sandy Balls for all Seasons

JEAN WESTLAKE

Anyone who has spent a summer holiday or two in the New Forest will probably be familiar with Sandy Balls Caravan Park, the celebrated destination of many a camper over the years.

Although traditionally the site of summer jollities, anyone who has enjoyed a holiday at Sandy Balls will no doubt be interested in Jean Westlake's recollection of the caravan park at a very different time of year.

It was crisp and cold: Kitty Trevelyan's family, my father and I walked between the caravans – singing as we went – to my mother's grave. We gathered round and stood silently looking over the valley below. It was dusk; this was Christmas Eve and we were carol singing. Quite spontaneously one of our number sang out in clear bell-like tone 'Ding-dong merrily on high, in heaven the bells are ringing'. We immediately responded and the blackbirds roosting in the rhododendron cover were unexpectedly jerked into song by this sudden explosion of sound. The carol ended and we were again quiet:

I found myself listening intently: Did I hear an answer from above? 'Ding dong merrily below, on earth the folk are singing . . .'

. . . 'And which carol would your mother have liked?' asked Kitty. 'The Holly and the Ivy' I said. 'She always liked the organ accompaniment.' 'I don't know about the organ, but we will do our best' she said. So together we all sang with real feeling into the gathering darkness – 'Of all the trees that are in the wood, the holly bears the crown'. The wind sighed gently as though the ice cold heavens above heard and received our carolling.

Walking back, an intense cold radiated from the starlit sky onto our upturned faces. Through the branches we saw the moon, a bright crescent moon on its back with a large star shining below it. Surely it was the Christmas star? We all stopped and looked up, lost in contemplation. I knew the reality of the Christ child, so soon to be born once again to us on Earth, I thought of the shepherds keeping watch over their flocks and the wise men who also looked up at this same sign, so long ago!

from

Old Men Remember Life on Victoria's Smaller Island

MARK WILLIAM NORTON

*The Isle of Wight, although now a county in its own right
(albeit the smallest in the country), has always been
inextricably linked to Hampshire and was for many years part
of the county. Mark William Norton was born on the Island in
the 1820s and, despite a brief time in London, lived on the
Island for over sixty years. A working man, who initially
earned his living as a labourer, Norman turned his hand to
many things and became a figure of some influence in local
society. He published writings on geology, contributed to the
local press and kept a diary until 1898, where he recorded this
incident which proves that some aspects of Christmas will never
change.*

A case of drink partaken too freely occurred to a smart young
woman, a cook in a gentleman's family near Niton Undercliff.

She had not been long in the situation and what took place occurred on Christmas Day when the members of families usually meet together. There were several newly married guests. One had brought with him a fine turkey, another a chine, which with other good things were handed over to the cook to prepare. The family had been to afternoon service at the village church, together with the servants. On their return they saw the cook stretched at full length before the fire drunk and incapable. The onlookers tried to rouse her but all they could do was exhort a few incoherent sentences to the effect that the Isle of Wight was the best place for everyone to come to, where a bottle of brandy was to be had for half a crown, and 'hurrah for the Isle of Wight!' The family had to dine off the chine without the turkey and the servants fared worse.

from

Memories of Bitterne

IRENE PILSON

Many of Hampshire's one-time villages have today become the suburbs of the county's expanding major cities, and Bitterne is one such village.

Southampton Stage Coach, 1833. From *Southampton Occasional Notes*, 1938

Now enveloped by the boundaries of Southampton, not too long ago Bitterne was a peaceful village, where two highways had met since 1796.

As traffic grew this junction became the notorious Bitterne fork and in 1969 became the subject of irate letters in the local evening paper, the Southern Echo.

In reply to the letters Irene Pilson, a resident of Bitterne for more than fifty years, sent a postcard to the Echo, *showing the so-called 'notorious fork' as she remembered it from her childhood – quiet, picturesque and devoid of traffic.*

The overwhelming response from fellow Bitternees eager to share their nostalgia for a fast-disappearing village prompted Mrs Pilson to write a book entitled Memories Of Bitterne.

*Here is an extract from the book in which Mrs Pilson recalls
Christmas during the First World War and the simple stocking
fillers which delighted local children each Christmas during
those sad years.*

Christmas During World War I

After Mr Hague's apples had been carefully wrapped and
stored away it was time to 'help' my mother mix her
Christmas puddings. My job was to stone the big, juicy valen-
cia raisins and to skin the blanched almonds. One of the local
superstitions was that one would enjoy a happy month for
every different Christmas pudding one tasted. So it was the
custom for each neighbour to offer a slice of her pudding and
receive the chance of a happy month in return. Nowadays
there would not be many chances of a happy month since so
many people prefer to buy their puddings . . .

In those days puddings were covered in pudding cloths
andboiled in a large saucepan kept for the purpose. Nowadays

Bitterne High Street in winter

they would be covered in cooking foil and steamed and even the cooking time would be considerably reduced if one of the modern pressure cookers was used. But who would then have thought of a special foil for cooking when even our delicious home-made jam was usually covered with thin writing paper dipped in milk to prevent the jam from going mouldy. No one had money to spare on unnecessary extras then.

Now it was time to buy the specially cut, coloured bundles of thin paper to make our Christmas paper chains. Our mother would make some nice thick flour and water paste such as paper hangers used before such things as Polycell ready-to-mix paste was invented.

It was child's play to paste the edges of a strip of paper and join the ends for the first link of the chain. Then another, different colour paper was slipped through the first link and joined up with the paste. By the end of the evening an industrious child would have a lengthy garland to show for her labours. Those with an artistic bent might confine the chains to a few toning or contrasting colours, but usually the younger child the more riotous the colours of the Christmas garland. As my father was a gifted artist, he would often do things to lift our decorations out of the ordinary.

Sometimes he would get some ivy leaves and thinly paint them with glue and then sprinkle them thickly with Epsom salt crystals. This gave a scintillating frosty effect. Then he would write some Christmas greetings in soap on the large mirror at the back of the sideboard and cover this with cotton wool to give a snowy look. He would then make intricate folds in large sheets of coloured decorating paper and fashion all kinds of decorations and bells. Those who could afford it bought such things ready made but we had much more fun watching our father make them from plain sheets of paper and cutting skill.

My father asked permission to bring home the empty wooden boxes from the cold storage at the Docks so that he

could make our Christmas toys with them. When he explained what he intended to make to the Dock Policeman, he was so impressed that he straightaway ordered a similar toy for his own little son. The toy in question was an excellent copy of an army lorry. My father made our toys so well that one could easily sit in the lorry. It was painted the proper army grey with a thin yellow line for decoration. The policeman was as delighted as my brother Tibby was when he received the finished article and said he would never have believed it was made from the rough old orange boxes, for my father had made every toy so smooth and safe for us.

Christmas Stocking Fillers in World War I

Although our Christmas toys were far less sophisticated than those of the 1980s they certainly lasted longer. Even now, I often come across some game or toy from those far-off days. One little puzzle which turned up in our stockings year after year in different guises was the small, square or round glass-fronted picture, with holes placed at strategic intervals into which one had to roll some little silver balls; like the ball bearings in bicycles. The picture might be of a clown's face or that of some animal. But it could always be guaranteed to keep us quiet for some time as we jiggled the little balls about.

Then there were the various sets of outfits on big white pieces of cardboard. A bus conductor's outfit, perhaps, complete with the peaked cap, the machine for clipping the tickets and the leather money bag for the fares; which could often, at Christmas time, be coaxed from the pockets of doting parents and relatives. Or it might be a milkman's equipment, again with a peaked cap and money bag. Cowboy sets included a big cowboy's hat and leather belt for his gun. Guns and pistols figured frequently as sock and stocking fillers.

Fortunately nylon had not been invented then so we wore long woollen black stockings or hand-knitted wool socks according to our age and sex. These would hold quite a lot of Christmas novelties. Pop guns costing six pence had a cork attached to a piece of green string. When you wanted to shoot someone, out would pop the cork on the end of the string. The toy pistol of pressed out tin came in several sizes from very tiny indeed, but they all fired caps which made them such an exciting toy for a small child. The caps could be bought in little round cardboard boxes; two for one old penny. These caps could also be used in another diabolical toy beloved of older lads. 'Bangers' as they were so rightly called, came in two parts. The cap was placed between the two sections, then wound round a piece of string which, as it quickly unwound, became a startling noise as the cap exploded. I am not sure if I have described its working correctly since I took care never to get close to anyone using a banger, but I have described its effect which was always guaranteed to make old ladies jump and wake sleeping babes.

Then there were the jack-in-the-box and vaulting clown toys. The latter could be persuaded to do all kinds of amazing acrobatic feats if one squeezed two pieces of wood in the right way. Spinning tops of gaily-coloured tin could sometimes be quite expensive toys, depending on their size and performance, and some of them hummed as they spun. There was of course the ever-popular set of lead soldiers in the long narrow box. There were also plenty of moulded lead toy animals for the farmyards. We had not realized how lethal the effect of lead could be. Little story books which could be rolled up to fit in the stockings and painting and crayoning books were also very popular. Pastels, as well as crayons, were used regularly by small children to create masterpieces, but I think today they would prefer to watch TV instead of sitting at the large scrubbed kitchen table with their pastels or paint boxes

making a fine old mess. There was always an apple and an orange in the toe of our stocking and some packets of sweets or chocolates to stay our hunger until breakfast time. A special treat were those little bundles of Cadbury's chocolates covered in different coloured tinfoil and looking like bundles of bricks tied up with gold or silver string. These cost two pence a bundle. There were also chocolate croquettes at the same price, usually in gold or silver tinfoil.

But one of the most memorable items, which was so cheap it turned up every year, was the packet of Magical Flowers. It was just a tiny square, transparent packet containing little pieces of dried wood. Not at all interesting to look at. The magic was the transformation when the contents of the packet were immersed in a glass of water. Then, 'before our very eyes', exotic flowers began to grow in the water. With an ethereal, fairy-like movement the fronds of the leaves would twist and turn so realistically that it really did seem as if some magician had conjured them from the air! So cheap too, that they turned up in every 'prizepacket' and 'lucky dip' at the sweet shop.

Clockwork toys of all kinds, now expensive collectors' items, were then very cheap. A trainset would cost about 1s. 11½d., but my father would never allow us to have these because he said they were cheap and nasty and dangerous because of the sharp edges of the wheels etc. We often envied our friends who were allowed to play with such toys.

Carolling

NORMAN GOODLAND

*Although the custom of Christmas carolling is not confined
to Hampshire alone, each county has its own peculiar version of
a tradition which seems to hold as much appeal for children
today as it has always done.*

*And who better to give us a taste of Christmas carolling
with a truly 'ampshire flavour, than popular local writer and
broadcaster Norman Goodland?*

'Carols is funny things! They bain't all to do wi' Christmas! If
you don't ring 'em out proper, they might not answer the
door, nor gie thee nar 'apence!'

Foster Father was delivering his annual lecture to the
Baughurst bell-ringers, of whom he was Captain. They practised in Foster Mother's scullery, on the handbells.

I remember them – big bewhiskered men, shirt sleeved
and leather belted, standing facing each other in a double
row. Flashing up the brass bells. Checking the swing with
broad thumb, to make them 'speak' in their clear, lucid
tones. It was all taken very seriously. Standards were high;
they had to be, to impress the gentry upon whom they
called.

They walked from Baughurst to Wolverton, back through
Ramsdell and Pamber End, and home through what was then
known as the 'gypsy' village of Tadley. Or made their way up

to Heath End, aiming for the high spot of the season –
Aldermaston Hall.

'We had to watch they sarvint galls!' Father once told me.
'They was always up to mischief!

'We was invited up to the hall oncest. We 'ad to go in
through the back, an' through the kitchens, y'see. An' we left
our 'ats in the kitchen along wi' they gals.

'We went in and give a tune or two to the Master and the
Mistress, and them as was there. They gie us a *sovereign*! They
told us to go back to the kitchens and Cook would gie us a
drink.

'So we done that. And when 'twas time to get on, they gals
was round the door away from the light. An' they wouldn't
gie us our 'ats until we give 'em a Christmas kiss.

'Waal – you never put yer 'at on inside a gentleman's 'ouse,
luk. So we put 'em on outside in the dark – so we didn't see
what was gwine on.

'Anyways. We went on down to the Hind's Head, t'other
end o' the street. We went in, took off our 'ats – an' everybody
started to laugh! We didn't know what to make on it! 'Til we
looked at each other – an' then we seed we all 'ad white 'air –
like a bunch of old men!

''Twas they sarvint gals! They'd put flour in our 'ats –
whiles we was a-carollin' for the Master!'

Father and his bell-ringers faced some competition from
other Christmas and New Year rounders – the village bands of
the time – The August Hill Drum and Fife Band. The
Temperence Bands; one from Tadley, one from Baughurst. But
it is said at the end of their rounds, the Temperence Bands
were not more temperate than Father and his bell-ringers,
when they came to clanking up the garden path well after
midnight, to collect their bicycles and wobble their ways
home!

Old Palace House Festivities

E.A. MITCHELL

In this article, first published in the Southern Daily Echo, *on Christmas Eve 1938, E.A. Mitchell describes the festivities enjoyed by generations of gentlefolk at Old Palace House, one of Southampton's oldest houses.*

Its sentimental reminiscence of the Victorian Christmas reminds us that Christmas is always a time for nostalgia, about Christmas past, if nothing else.

There are some places in Southampton in which succeeding generations have eaten Christmas dinner for centuries. This does not, of course, apply to all our ancient buildings, because not all have been dwelling houses. But it applies to our oldest houses, and it applies notably to Tudor House. What a strange and moving pageant it would be if there were a magician among us who could tomorrow summon up in the rooms of that ancient residence some of the Christmas scenes from the past. They would carry us back four, five, six – we cannot tell quite how many – hundred years, because, although its surviving architecture belongs to the Tudor period (there is, of course, the famous tradition that Henry VIII and Anne Boleyn lodged there during a visit to Southampton), there are

foundations which suggest an earlier origin. Now the old place is a museum and, interesting as it is, has no accommodation any more for family intimacies.

These Tudor House Christmases ceased a quarter of a century ago, for it was then that Tudor House became Tudor House. Previously it had been Old Palace House, the name having its origin in the tradition that it was once a portion of a palace belonging to King John. But in modern times it was Victorian family life which provided Old Palace House with some of its most delightful Christmas parties. The Victorians were specially devoted to family life, and cherished the sentiment attaching to it. Some of us remember that family life well; think of it, in the midst of this hurrying, changing modern world, with affection and a faint shadow of regret. Family relations and the relations of friendships in those days were deeply felt. When they were broken by death or distance the memories were encouraged to linger.

The Old Palace House, Southampton. From *Southampton Occasional Notes*, 1938

How vividly the snatch of an old Victorian song can bring back the Victorian atmosphere with visions of once familiar faces and old happenings, long forgotten.

That is why in this little sketch of a Victorian family Christmas in Tudor House I venture to introduce that once popular song *Far Away*, which in words, music, and sentiment is so characteristic of the period. My Victorian readers will remember it well. Everybody knew this song. It was much sung at Christmas parties although, curiously enough, the words were from *Summer Songs of Country Life*. They are not high-class poetry, but they are perfectly representative of a certain Victorian mood. Here they are:

> Where is now the merry party
> I remember long ago,
> Laughing round the Christmas fire
> Brightened by its ruddy glow?
> Or in summer's balmy evenings
> In the field upon the hay –
> They have all dispersed and wandered
> Far away, far away.
>
> Some have gone to land distant,
> And with strangers made their home;
> Some upon the world of waters
> All their lives are forced to roam.
> Some are gone from us forever
> Longer here they might not stay
> They have reached a fairer region
> Far away, far away.
>
> There are still some few remaining
> Who remind us of the past,
> But they change, as all things change here –

Nothing in the world can last!
Years roll on and pass forever:
What is coming who can say?
'Ere this closes many may be
Far away, far away.

The Bargate, with The Coachmakers' Arms. A drawing by Heywood
Sumner, 1880. From *Southampton Occasional Notes*, 1938

On the Antiquity of Twelfth Day

FROM *THE COUNTY MAGAZINE*

*Among the various phenomena which were discussed and
reported in* The County Magazine *in 1788, there appeared
the following analysis on the custom of Twelfth Night.*

*Whether the gentlefolk of Hampshire were any the wiser
after reading the piece two hundred years ago is a moot point,
but the modern reader will, I am sure, find the style
entertaining if rather confused.*

Collier in his Ecclesiastical History, vol. i. page 163, sees to
account in a satisfactory manner for the name of twelfth day.
'In the days of King Alfred a law was made in relation to
Holidays, by virtue of which the twelve days after the nativity
of our Saviour were made Festivals.'

That our crowned heads were zealous in these pastimes may
be collected from innumerable instances upon record, and probably thence was derived the ceremony of choosing King and
Queen: for our monarchs themselves went disguised to the
houses of their courtiers: and their nobles in return frequently
visited the palace in masquerade on the same occasion.

Hector Boethius relates that 'King Arthur kept with his
nobles at York a very prophane Christmas for thirteen days

together, including Christmas day, and that such jollity and feasting then had its origin from him'.

We read in Fabian's Chronicle, temp. Henry IV 'In which passe tyme the Duke of Amnarle, of Surrey, and of Exeter, with the Earl of Salesbury, and Gloucestyr, with other of their affynyte, made provysion for a dysguysynge, or mummery to be shewed to the Kinge upon Twelfth Nyght, and the tyme was near at hande, and all thynge ready for the fame. Upon the sayd twelfth day came secretlye unto the Kinge, the Duke of Armnarle, and shewed to him, that he wyth the other Lords aforenemed, were appointed to sle hym in the time of the fore sayd dysguysynge, &c.'

Stowe has preserved an account of a remarkable Mummery, 1377, made by the citizens for disport of the young Prince Richard, son to the Black Prince. One hundred and thirty

The North Waltham Mummers, near Basingstoke, 1948

citizens disguised and well-horsed, in a Mummery, with sound of trumpets, sackbuts, cornets, shalmes and other minstrels, and innumerable torch-lights of wax, rode to Kennington, near Lambeth, where the young prince was – and contrived to lose to him at dice, some jewels, rings and gold.

On this day the eastern magi were led by the star to pay their devotions to our saviour; being the twelfth day after nativity it is called Twelfth Day.

There were various customs in various places appropriated to this day. In the academies of Germany, one of the students is chosen as king and a magnificent entertainment provided for him. This is evidently borrowed from the Roman Saturnaliai, when the masters gave entertainment to their servants, and waited upon them. This was formerly practised in our Universities, but it is now laid aside. As Christmas is generally understood to terminate on this day, it is commonly celebrated with more festivity amongst those who are attached to Christmas-cheer. In the calendars of the Romish Church, against this day you often find it written 'Reges fabis creantur'. In the twelfth cake there was a bean, and, in division of it, he whose portion the bean was, was saluted as king. Formerly each mistress of a family made the cake herself; it was necessary that it should be compounded of flour, honey, ginger, and pepper; whilst she was kneading it, she was to put a piece of money into it. The cake was divided into as many parts as there were persons in the family and whoever found the money in his cake was saluted as King.

The Mummer's Play

FROM *IT HAPPENED IN HAMPSHIRE*

The Mummer's Play, which is still performed at Christmas in various villages throughout the county, is a genuine survivor from the Middle Ages. Thought to date from the twelfth century the Mummer's Play has various forms which change from village to village, but the overriding theme is that of death and rebirth.

The scripts of individual plays were handed down by word of mouth from one generation to the next so, although ancient in origin, there is little evidence of the Mummer's Play until more recent times when various organizations and individuals took it upon themselves to record these plays for posterity.

The Hampshire Federation of Women's Institutes was one such organization and in 1936 excerpts of Mummer's Plays from Woodhay, Boldre and Twyford appeared in the Federation's famous book It Happened In Hampshire, *along with the entire Yately Mummer's Play which is reproduced here.*

Yately Mummers

First to enter, Father Christmas

'In comes I, old Father Christmas, Christmas welcome or not

I hope old Father Christmas will never be forgot,

for in this room there shall be shown
The most dreadful battle that ever was known.
So walk in King George, with thy free heart, and see if thou can
claim peace on thine own part.'

King George
'In comes I, King George, the man of courage bold,
With this broad sword and spear I won ten crowns of gold.
It was me who fought that fiery dragon and drove him to be slaughtered,
And by the means of that, I won the King of Egypt's daughter.
Therefore let any man enter this room, I will act with the small dust,
And afterwards send him to the cookshop,
To be made into mince pie crust.'

1st Turkey Snipe (Turkish knight originally)
'In comes I, bold Turkey snipe,
From Turkey land I've come to fight.
I'll fight the man of courage bold, if his blood's hot I'll quickly make it cold.'

King George
'Ho, Ho, my little fellow, you are talking rather bold,
Just like the little Turks, that, I have been told.
Therefore Turkey Snipe, pull your sword out and fight, pull out your purse and pay,
We will have satisfaction before we go away.'

Turkey Snipe
'There is no satisfaction at all
For my head is made of iron,

71

The Andover Mummers in 1936

And my body is lined with steel,
And I'll fight King George and see
Which on this ground shall fall.'

2nd Turkey Snipe
'King George, King George, what hast thou done.
Thou hast cut and slain my brother, just like the evening
sun,
Is there a noble doctor to be found
That can cure this man lies bleeding on the ground.'

The doctor
'Yes you see there is a noble doctor to be found
Can cure that man lies bleeding on the ground.'

2nd Turkey Snipe
'What is your fee, Doctor?'

Doctor
'Ten guineas is my fee, ten pounds I'll take of thee.'

2nd Turkey Snipe
'Take it doctor, what can thou cure, doctor?'

Doctor
'I can cure Hipsy, Pipsy, Palsy and the Gout,
That's a Roman pain runs in and out.
A broken leg or broken arm,
I'll quickly set it together again.
Beside all that bring me a woman three score and ten,
If she hasn't a tooth in her head
I'll soon make her young and sound again.'

2nd Turkey Snipe
'Is all this true, doctor, what thou has been talking about?'

Doctor
'Yes I am not one of these little quack doctors go about telling you this thing and that thing, who would tell you as many lies in five minutes as I would in seven years. What I do, I do before your eyes. It is hard if you can't believe your own eyes.'

2nd Turkey Snipe
'It is doctor.'

Doctor

'I have a little bottle by my side, that I call Golden False Drops. One drop on the tip of his tongue and another on his crown, will strike him through the body and rise him from the ground.'

King George

'Arise, arise, thou cowardly dog, and go back to your own country and tell them what old England's done, tell them they can fight ten thousand better men than thee.'

2nd Turkey Snipe

'When you have got your mates with you.'

Johnny Jack

'In comes I, little Johnny Jack,
My wife and family on my back.
My family's large, my wife so small.
And I am the father of them all.
Roast beef, plum pudding and mince pies,
Who likes that better than old Father Christmas and I.
Nobody.
A jug of your Christmas Ale sir,
Will make us merry and sing.
Money in our pockets is a very fine thing.
So ladies and gentlemen, be at your ease
And give us poor Mummers just what you please.'

from

An Old Woman's Outlook

CHARLOTTE YONGE

Born in Otterbourne in 1823, Charlotte Yonge spent most of her life in the village where, despite her sheltered rural existence, she became a prolific novelist whose popularity arose from her wonderful ability to establish an immediate rapport with her readers.

Extraordinarily devoted to her family, and to Hampshire, Yonge's novels are dominated by her strong sense of filial obedience and her belief in a quiet, pastoral way of life.

Having produced many successful novels she published her memoirs, entitled An Old Woman's Outlook on a Hampshire Village, *at the age of sixty-nine. They included the following chapter devoted to the month of December which provides a charming calendar of rural life leading up to Christmas.*

December sets in usually with mild weather, a prolongation of November fogs, sparing all the plants that survived the October frost, and even encouraging a few to blossom.

Primroses put out a few short-stemmed flowers, which cock-
neys in the country think wonderful enough to write to the
papers about. Now and then a branch of pear tree, if it have
been nipped in the summer, attempts to blossom, but is con-
sidered 'unlucky'.

Chrysanthemums have just attained to their full beauty; they
are at present the chief subjects of gardeners' transformations.
The old yellow daisy-like flower has been persuaded into inter-
minable shapes and shades, and the varieties have almost as long
a list of names as the roses. Here they are white, and curled at
the tips, forming perfect snowballs, or star-like and straggling,
or delicate sulphur-coloured, or of every shade of crimson, sometimes yellow above and crimson beneath – pompon when small
and compact, Japanese when large and straggling – or with
curled points, and lately with a tendency – by way of variety –
to give up the central strap-shaped petals and revert to the daisy-
like eye of the original flower. In all plants capable of variations
there is first an original wild perfect adaptation and grace; there
is next a sort of civilised beauty; and there is lastly a gardener's
freak worked up into exaggeration for the sake of exhibition.
Still we will not quarrel with the flower available for church decoration, lasting long, both gathered and ungathered, and brightening us up far into the winter.

Preferable, however, are the Christmas roses which do not
lend themselves to important diversities. Indeed, what we
regard as the flower is only the bracts. The petals are odd little horned things, almost mixed up with the stamens. They
really are, by their Latin name, *Helleborus niger*, and belong to
a poisonous race, whose name has none of the associations of
the Christmas rose.

If it is an open winter, we have good hope of plenty of
berries; but as to the belief that their number foretells hard
weather, it rather points back to the absence of killing frosts
at their blossoming time in the spring, when the holly ought

to be threaded over with tiny white four-petalled, four-stamened flowers, to give place to the bright coral berries which nothing equals. 'Holly' is really 'holy'. The old people here used to call a bush without berries 'holm', in contra-distinction, and sometimes a fine branch is termed 'Christmas'. Southey made us remark how the prickly leaves cease as the tree reaches a height beyond the reach of cattle, breathing a wish that –

> So the calm temper of my age may be
> Like the high leaves upon the holly tree.

One of the most simple as well as deep poems in the *Lyra Innocentium* was prompted by the exclamation of a little girl, who, looking into the church before the decorations were put up, exclaimed in disappointment, 'No Christmas here!' –

> What if that little maiden's Lord,
> That awful Child on Mary's knee,
> Even now take up the accusing word,
> 'No Christmas here I see.
>
> 'Where are the fruits I yearly seek,
> As holy seasons pass away;
> Eyes turned from ill, lips pure and meek,
> A heart that strives to pray?
>
> 'Where are the glad and artless smiles,
> Like clustering hollies, seen afar
> At eve along the o'ershadowed aisles,
> With the first twilight star?'

Holly, even in berryless years, is to my mind better alone than with any sham imitations of berries, though a scarlet tie

for the sprays may be effective and allowable. Variegated holly, especially where a few leaves are ivory-white, is a great assistance in brightening, but I do not love yellow-berried holly.

Cotoneaster, though the wreaths of white blossoms are pretty against the wall, and the little red berries still more so, does not catch the light enough to be effective on these dark days. Even the clusters of Eccremocarpus, though looking brilliant out of doors, do not *tell* in church.

Ivy (*Hedera helix*) is the legitimate companion and rival of holly – everywhere cheerful, even in decay, and putting out its green heads of blossom so late in the year that the black berries are only ripe in time to keep the store which the birds have not gathered into barns. These heads only begin to be put forth after the ivy has ceased to climb, and produces branches and leaves of an unbroken pointed egg-shape, entirely different from the deeply divided and wonderfully varying leaves with which it climbs. To collect the different forms of ivy leaves to be met with in a walk is one of the diversions I should recommend to those who are unlucky enough to think a country walk in autumn or winter dull.

A berry larger than the holly and as beautiful, but seldom plentiful enough to be of much use, belongs to the Butcher's-broom, or Kneeholm (*Ruscus aculeatus*) – a very curious plant, related, of all families in the world, to the asparagus. Only the little green flowers are divided into sexes on the same plant, and have no stems, lying flat on the dark green, pointed, spine-ended leaves, where the fertile ones leave a very handsome red berry. It grows wild upon heaths, and is rare, but probably was once more common than now. The so-called Alexandrian laurel which makes useful wreaths is also a *Ruscus*; but it blossoms at the end of its sprays, and does not ripen fruit in this climate. Some say it is really the bay or laurel of which the wreath of successful poets was composed,

and it is certainly more convenient for the purpose than the fragrant bay.

The other peculiarly Christmas plant, Mistletoe (*Viscus albatus*), is banished from our churches on account of the associations, sometimes merely merry, but too often degenerating into vulgarity and rudeness, which make all the lads go about with a sprig of mistletoe in their hats. The tales of Druid worship are, as we all know, intimately connected with the mistletoe, especially with the oak-grown plant, probably from its extreme rarity; for though it is frequent upon ash and apple trees, it is hardly ever found on oaks. The Druid solemnity of cutting it down with a golden knife, and catching it in a white cloth, is well known. It used to be found on oaks at Norwood when that was a wood, and being supposed to be medicinal when so growing, was sometimes cut down for apothecaries in London. But the men who meddled with it were said always to fall lame or become blind of an eye! Its French name, *gui*, is probably Celtic.

Its place in Norse myths is equally noted. It was the exception when Freya charmed all minerals, plants, and animals from harming Baldur, and therefore Loki pointed with it the arrow which he persuaded blind Hodur to shoot at the white deity. Whether it was from some lingering connection with its being the means of Baldur's death is not known, but there was a Christian legend that it had been a fine tree till it furnished the wood of the Cross, in expiation of which it became the strange imperfect plant that it now seems. In some parts of France it is called *l'herbe à la Croix*, and it was thought to be a spell against evil spirits, as well as a cure for epilepsy and many other diseases.

Scarcely noticed in the early part of the year, when the apple trees are in full leaf, it comes into full prominence when they are stripped, hanging with its yellow-green clusters of branches from the limbs. The root is firmly embedded in the

fibre of the tree; the stem is repeatedly forked, a thickened ring at each fork. The leaves are stemless, leathery, of the same uniform yellow-green, the flowers also stemless, perched within the forks and monœcious – the female ones giving place to a soft white berry, which is said to missel or soil the toes of the missel-thrush, thus naming both bird and bush, though the derivation is not very satisfactory.

It is not ornamental enough to be a loss to our church decorations. I remember many phases of them – the sticking, by the clerk, of holly boughs into the holes made on purpose in the ancient pews, and the gradual interference of the young ladies, who came timidly and felt it an exceeding honour and privilege to be allowed to assist, while old people doubted of the lawfulness and expedience of using flowers at all.

An honour and privilege it is still to work for the house of God and beautify the place of His sanctuary; but now that it has become a matter of course, how many clerical houses feel it a burthen and perplexity, while among the workers there is danger of irreverence, and difficulties of temper, and clashing taste. Well, in this world, first it is a point to do the thing, next to do it in the right way.

St Thomas's Day ushers in Christmas. 'Pray, sir,' asked a boy, 'did they give St Thomas the shortest day because he was not a very good saint?' That St Thomas is compensated in the Antipodes had not occurred to him.

Here, as in some other Hampshire villages, St Thomas's Day is spent by all the poorer women in what they call 'gooding' – going from house to house to receive something towards the Christmas dinner. A shilling to each widow, and sixpence to each wife, is the traditional amount; but hardly any one keeps up the dole, since modern changes have come in, and neither squires, farmers, nor peasants are in the old semi-feudal connection. In most places some other form of Christmas gift has been substituted, though nowhere can

New Forest gypsies, 1965

those questions which are the pain of almsgiving be avoided –
who is too well-off, and, on the other hand, who ought not to
be helped for fear of fostering evil and deceit? The traditional
dole, however, carried no stigma of beggary.

Another ordinance of St Thomas's Feast was the arrival of certain musical gipsies. 'It's the Lees!' has been the answer when
asking the cause of an outbreak of drumming and the like; but
this likewise has nearly come to an end, and the genuine gipsy is
not a very frequent creature. Moreover, he travels no longer in a
picturesque, ramshackle tilted cart, where the red-kerchiefed
mother and bright-eyed, brown-faced children look out as from
a bower, but in a yellow van, with a stove-pipe protruding from
it. And he often has quarters in a town for the winter.

One genuine family was here some years ago, of thorough
gipsy blood. A woman was very ill, and a kind of gentleman
let them remain in his field and sent broth and wine. They

were strictly honest, and even refused offers of help from other quarters, saying that they were fully provided for. The woman died, and they lamented her with loud cries like Easterns. They talked of putting up a stone to her, but have never done so. Her name was Gerania.

This gipsy music is not connected with carols. Those carols, in the old time, had a flavour of wild beauty about them. I remember standing in the shrubbery in the dark, with stars overhead, and snatches of song floating on the wind from every quarter, giving a sense of Christmas joy.

But they needed to be heard at a distance. Near at hand the children, then utterly untrained in voice, sang like ballad-singers, generally –

While shepherds watched their flocks by night;

The interior of a New Forest gypsy's caravan, 1973

but sometimes that notable carol where Lazarus is described among the dogs –

> He had no strength to drive them off,
> And so – and so they licked his sores;

and finally 'Divers' (as he was always called) sits on a serpent's knee!

The shrill thin voices of the children were only ignorantly irreverent, but there were parties of boisterous lads or idle men as ignorant, more profane, and sometimes half-tipsy, and on the way to be entirely so.

The practice had to be reformed. Picturesqueness is apt not to bear close inspection, and propriety and reverence must be enforced even through primness and a little hard-heartedness. So now the children of a fit age are taught well-chosen carols, and go round under the surveillance of the master and mistress, and the money-box is divided at the end, and produces more than the chance pence thrown at haphazard and not at all after the change is exhausted; and the children, who do not remember the old days of licence, greatly delight in their rounds.

The elders are, or ought to be, in the choir, and have a regular festival supper; and to the undesirable, it is really best to turn a deaf ear.

Christmas, unless the salt of life be there, grows sadder as we grow older, and it is one of the stock moralisings of the worldly sort to murmur at being expected to be merry by rule, to make presents, pay bills, and partake of indigestible fare.

The conventional Christmas of illustrated papers and Christmas cards is only too apt to foster this more outward phase of the festival, of which the pudding wreathed with holly is the symbol. To keep the day primarily as the Birthday of the Lord, rejoicing evermore, because He is close at hand, is the only way to keep the rejoicing through life, and hinder

the external festivities from becoming hollow and weary. So may the 'Outlook', going beyond the pleasures around and the delights of nature, illuminate them all with a brighter light than that which otherwise ever shone on sea or land.

The Oxen and Old Christmas Eve

THOMAS HARDY AND BERT BUTLER

The legend that farm animals kneel down in reverence to the baby Jesus on Christmas Eve is by no means restricted to Hampshire, although the following two poems show that it was a belief widely held throughout the county.

The first poem, written in 1915, is one of Thomas Hardy's most famous poems and has that poignant sense of innocence lost which dominates his work.

The second poem entitled 'Old Christmas Eve', by Bert Butler, while lacking the high-brow status of Hardy's poem, is perhaps a closer representation of local curiosity about the custom. It first appeared in the 1870s and was reprinted, together with its informative introduction, in Hampshire and Wessex Life, *1974.*

Christmas Eve, and twelve of the clock.
'Now they are all on their knees,'
An elder said as we sat in a flock
By the embers in hearthside ease.

We pictured the meek mild creatures where
They dwelt in their strawy pen,
Nor did it occur to one of us there
To doubt they were kneeling then.

So fair a fancy few would weave
In these years! Yet, I feel,
If someone said on Christmas Eve,
'Come; see the oxen kneel

'In the lonely barton by yonder coomb
Our childhood used to know,'
I should go with him in the gloom,
Hoping it might be so.

Many years ago it was widely believed that at midnight on
Christmas Eve, cattle went down on their knees in reverence
to the infant Christ. The belief may have originated in the fif-
teenth century when Sannazarius, a Latin poet, wrote a poem
about the Nativity in which he referred to the Virgin wrapping up the new-born infant, the cattle 'cherishing him with
their breath', and an ox and an ass 'falling on their knees'.
However it began, there were those who took it as a fact and
those who regarded it as merely superstition. To resolve their
own doubts about it, John and William Staite of the Lodge
Farm, on the Sudeley estate, determined one year to put it to
the test. On Christmas Eve they went into their cow-house at
midnight – and found all their cattle lying down, comfortably
settled for the night. That appeared to be that. What they had

forgotten, however, was that the proper time for the occurrence was not Christmas Eve but *OLD* Christmas Eve – midnight on January 5/6 – as the lines below tell . . .

> I'm zure the old time is the right,
> I'm zure on't, let whoe'er deny it,
> I'll tell 'e why I be so zure:
> 'Twere thirty year agoo or moore;
> 'Twere when I worked for Farmer Gray
> The night afore Old Christmas Day.
> One o' our cows wer tuk quite bad,
> And to look a'ter her I had.
> Zoo I bid up we her thick night,
> And loo! I had a desperate fright,
> Fer jist as 'twere past twelve o'clock,
> I found the very cow-staall rock.
> Our bad cow ris up from the ground;
> Bowed to the east, and then kneel'd down
> I looked round the staal to see
> If t'others kneel'd as well as she,
> And zure enough among 'em ell
> (There were dree and thirty in the staall)
> Not one wer standen, but I found
> Every one 'o 'em were kneel'd down.
> I run'd in a doors wi' speed
> To tell my master what I'd seed.
> Zed he, ye needen make a fuss and be afeered,
> For he'd often heered folks say
> That cows kneel'd the night afore ole Christmas Day,
> Zoo I'm zure the old time is the right,
> I'm zure on't, let whoeer ool deny it.

The Man Who Lost Christmas

PHILIP KLITZ

In 1850 Philip Klitz published From Sketches of Life, Character and Scenery in the New Forest, *a collection of tales 'rural, domestic, legendary and humorous', based on his own experiences of life in the New Forest. In his preface to the book, Klitz, a composer by occupation, recounts how the publication came into being.*

'In travelling out of his accustomed line of composition, the Author of the following Sketches would briefly explain to the Reader (whose kind indulgence he entreats), the casual circumstances from which they had their origin. In the course of a summer-day's ramble in the Forest, in the company of an esteemed friend, the writer related to his companion the substance of some of these stories, with the incidents of which he had become familiar by lengthened residence in a Forest-town, and by professional visits throughout the entire district. His auditor suggested that the tales which had been told him might furnish themes for more lasting record by the pen; and thus encouraged, he diverted that instrument from its wonted practice among crochets and quavers and turned it to "literary" uses.'

It is difficult to determine whether the following tale about Peter Batt, the Man Who Lost Christmas, is fact or fiction, but it is certainly a quaint and charming story based on Klitz's first-hand experience of New Forest life in the last century.

87

Of all the days in the three hundred and sixty-five, no one was ever so replete with joy and happiness to Peter Batt as the Twenty-fifth of December. With him it had been a red-letter day through life. As a child he frisked and gambolled on his father's hearth; as a youth he had joined in all the gaieties and festivities which that particular period of the year affords; and as a husband and father, Peter had always contrived to indulge, on this day, in the luxuries of the season. For many years he had never failed, by honest and patient industry, to provide hearty and cheerful fare for himself and those dependent on him; and each successive Christmas-day brought with it some new delight or gratification. Truly Peter enjoyed himself to his heart's content, and was never more happy than when surrounded by those he loved; who with their smiling faces warmed and cheered his heart, as they did justice to his kindness and hospitality. Peter was like unto all things human. Honest, simple-hearted Peter had his share of what philosophers (who of course never possess it themselves) call vanity. What! a man living in one of the most retired nooks in the kingdom – a man who had seen and enjoyed upwards of fifty Christmas-days! – the father of six children and husband of Sally Batt, whose tongue might take the pride out of any man – pooh, pooh! Nay, reader, but it was even so! Among the many moral infirmities which poor human nature is heir to, vanity was a besetting fault of poor Peter: but let not the reader labour under the erroneous idea that it was personal vanity on the part of Peter, for here is his picture. From the soles of his feet to the crown of his head, we may fairly estimate a structure of about five feet five, habited with excellent neatness and precision – for it is Christmas-day, and Peter has donned his best. See how brilliantly his shoes glisten beneath the neat black gaiter surmounting them! Observe the snowy whiteness of the cotton stockings which enclose his well-proportioned lower limbs, again surmounted by the neat

black velveteen continuations. A waggish visitor from the great city once ventured to compare Peter's style of dress to the alternate colours of the magpie; but his witticism failed – Peter stood too high in the estimation of his rural friends to be affected by such observations. Then see the admirable keeping of the picture – how these are relieved by the square homely-cut of his single but straight-breasted snuff-brown coat, with large yellow metal buttons and upright collar! Well, Peter; I see nothing in thee or thy coat whereof an honest Englishman need feel ashamed: thy well-set frame bespeaks thee a man of strength, and doubtless thy sinewy arm and hardened hand have wrought worthily for thee and thine. And then thy good-tempered face, and twinkling grey eyes, whereof one hath a southerly inclination and the other an affection for the north: and withal, thy venerable bald pate. – Who shall say thou art not worthy of praise? But where gottest thou that self-satisfied air? Ah! I forget, it is Christmas-day, and thy destiny is to fulfil certain duties, whereof more anon. Say, then, to what conclusion can we arrive as to the cause of our hero's vain-glory? Truly he is proud of his six children, and well he may be – for where shall we find four sons and two daughters, in one family, more healthy, or more attentive and dutiful to their parents. Then his wife, his Sally! was there such another housewife in the whole village? To be sure, Sally had a tongue, as well as a will of her own; and sometimes treated honest Peter with what he facetiously called chin-music, but not after the manner of Michael Boai. Yet, take her for all in all, Sally was a good wife, mother, friend, and neighbour; and as Peter

> Was to her faults a little blind,
> And to her virtues very kind,

they jogged on harmoniously together, and enjoyed a very fair proportion of domestic happiness.

But it is necessary, without further prologue, to acquaint the reader with the mainspring of Peter's ambition, and to that end I would direct his observation to that smaller specimen of button which dangles at a little distance from the bright, large, yellow row, that ornaments his snuff-brown coat. On that tiny button 'hangs our tale', for thereon is wont to depend the object of his devout affection – the rival of mistress Batt in her husband's love – his ever-petted baby – his *bassoon*! Assume, O Reader, inexperienced in the fervent passion which amateur members of the Orphean family often feel for that particular instrument through which (in their own opinion) they 'discourse most eloquent music' – assume, I pray thee, no sceptical air at this assurance, that Peter Batt – worthy man, good husband as he was – did now and then prefer the fellowship of his bassoon to that of Sally – did sometimes find *its* voice the more enchanting of the two. Did she first learn to love him, I wonder, as with distended cheeks he strove to render his wooden idol lovely in *her* eyes? Madame de Stael somewhere suggests the impossibility of a woman's love being kindled in favour of a man performing on the bassoon; and Sally has therefore an opportunity of acquiring fame by denying (if she is able) the insinuation of the celebrated Frenchwoman.

For forty years, as man and boy, had Peter Batt been a prominent member of our village church choir. He had developed all the varieties to which male voices are subject, and as he was ambitious of reputation, the whole parish had the benefit of his vocal powers. Unfortunately, perhaps, for Peter's future fame as a singer, his father – who was also a bassoon-player – was too much addicted to the habit of flattering his son's 'childish treble', not hesitating in the boy's presence to declare that Peter had 'a stounden voice', and that 'ye cou'd hear un down t' bridge' – a distance of nearly half a mile. The natural consequence of this encomium was, that Peter wished

to make himself heard *beyond* the bridge, and to that end so shrieked and squalled as ultimately to *crack* his voice irreparably; and notwithstanding all his after efforts, he never could be certain whether the note he were about to sound would prove itself a tenor, counter, or bass note. This was sadly thwarting the aspirant for fame; but when he found that all hope of eminence in that line was quite shut out, he one day, in sheer despair, took down from the bacon-rack (where it had been placed since his father's death) the family bassoon. I should here mention that Peter's common avocation was that of a wheelwright, as his father's had been before him; and I would allude also to a striking historic coincidence, to show why great things might not, under more favourable auspices, have resulted from Peter's cultivation of music. Haydn, the first great symphonist that Germany produced, was the son of a village wheelwright, and his father was also musical: I am not aware, certainly, that he practised the bassoon; but suffice it that he instilled a love of music into his son, who displayed such early genius, and extreme beauty of voice, as to attract the attention of all his friends and neighbours. My readers will recollect the estimation in which the senior Batt held the vocal abilities of his son and heir: doubtless this admiration extended itself pretty generally through the parish, and but for the non-existence of certain national facilities, it is possible that England also might have produced a symphonist. With the music-loving Germans it always formed an integral feature in their system of education; an indispensable requisite in the qualifications of even a village schoolmaster in Germany is a knowledge of music – and here was the advantage which Haydn possessed over our hero, for attracted by the beauty of his voice, we find the singing master of the royal chapel of St Stephen's, in Vienna, visiting the schoolmaster to hear his favourite pupil; the consequence of which was, that Haydn was at once removed to the chapel, where he received a

regular musical education; and Germany had the honour of fostering the genius of this illustrious composer. Now, had corresponding advantages been presented in dear Old England, one thing is certain – old Michael Drodge would not have presided over the ploddings of Peter when a student; for poor old Michael in the first place was nearly deaf; in the second, had no knowledge of music, intuitive or acquired; and lastly, held it in supreme contempt, since nature had deprived him of the power of appreciating it. But for these drawbacks is it not *possible* that Peter Batt might have attained celebrity as a composer? [Between ourselves, he did make one experiment – with what effect the sequel will show.] But I could not resist this opportunity of remarking on the characteristic differences of the two nations, as it regards music.

Having shown the musical as well as natural origin of our hero, we will now trace him through his earlier years, when, having completed the routine of his education, he commenced his occupation as a wheelwright, under his father. Be it known then that he secured the confidence and esteem of all his neighbours; and that, as the old man's infirmities increased, so did Peter's responsibilities. At length his father died, just as Peter was competent to carry on the business. Behold him now, his own master, with a thriving trade, and no incumbrance – free to make choice of a wife. Under such circumstances, he felt it impossible to resist the influence of his old schoolmaster's daughter, Sally, or rather 'Mistress' Drodge, as she was called by the housekeeper at the manor-house, in which establishment she filled the important situation of lady's maid, and with her smart cap and neat attire, quite unsettled the heart of Peter. I have before stated that he resorted to the bassoon, hopeless of ever becoming a singer; – this was subsequently to his father's death. The fact is, he had been so constant an attendant of the village choir, that he felt quite unhappy in being incapacitated from joining in its

performances. This induced him to great exertions (for he was still ambitious) and he therefore practised whenever an opportunity offered. Could the reader have heard him run up and down the instrument, from the lowest note to the highest, and then close in a cadence of great force and power on the lowest E flat, which he held with a 'stounden' tenacity and tone, he would have been convinced of the strength of his lungs, if not of the purity of his taste. Peter was greatly admired – perhaps rather from the extraordinary loudness of his performance than the delicacy of his expression; but in the particular line he had chosen he could do more than many of the first solo players who have distinguished themselves as bassoonists: he could play the 'College Hornpipe', 'Country Bumpkin', or 'Sir Roger de Coverley', to thirty couples up and down, in the same evening; and if that is not a pretty good proof of the strength of his lungs, I know not what is. If then 'Music hath charms to soothe the *savage* breast', and if our hero was thus renowned as one of her most favoured votaries, can it be supposed that Sarah Drodge could attend the village church every Sunday, and hear unmoved of the proficiency of Peter Batt? How often did Peter, in the acme of his best achievements direct his angular orbs of vision into the pew that contained the tender object of his passion! To be sure it required some slight acquaintance with Peter's eyes to ascertain their exact direction; but Sarah knew the precise degree of their inclination, and I incline to think – despite the assertions of Madame de Stael – that his inflated cheeks and energetic strains made a deep impression on her heart. To her, Peter Batt, with his bassoon, was a most interesting, if not a romantic specimen of humanity. He had often wished for an opportunity of breathing forth his tender aspirations and vows of eternal love and constancy, when a circumstance occurred that put him at once at rest as to the reciprocity of their feelings.

It has been a custom, from time immemorial, for the choir of the parish church (which respected body of men and boys was under the especial direction of our hero), to perambulate the village during Christmas-eve, singing in and before the houses of the most respectable of the inhabitants, the carols and anthems appropriate to the season: this generally took up a great portion of the night; and at church, on the following day, the same were repeated to the admiration of a very full congregation. Of course this was an 'event' to all the members of the choir in general, and to Peter Batt in particular. On the evening of Christmas-day the choir was always invited up to the manor-house, where the good squire, his family, his visitors, and household, were accustomed to assemble in the hall – some to witness and others to join in the merry-makings which prevailed at this merry period. The performances of the choir were interspersed with the general amusements, which were necessarily suspended for a time, during the business of refreshment; and on one occasion – big with the fate of Mrs Drodge and Peter Batt – by accident or connivance those two personages found themselves seated side by side at the squire's hospitable board. Now was it that Peter felt his waistcoat heave – particularly on the heart's side – with emotions struggling for utterance, which must, alas! continue to struggle, at least till after supper, and then —— ! Whether Mrs Drodge's gentle bosom were agitated by sympathetic feelings, I can't affirm so confidently as I could wish; but I still have reasons for thinking that her state of mind was similar to that of a person conscious that a great and long-expected crisis is now close at hand. And so indeed it was. By-and-by it became Peter's turn, in the course of 'blind-buff', with sealed eyes to pursue – whom, I wonder? For whose accents did he listen with strained ears, and with fixed design – could he but make that capture – to lead his prize beneath the hanging mistletoe, and there —— ? Did Sally Drodge, with that 'diplomacy'

intuitive (as we have before asserted) to lovers – did Sally permit that half-cough to escape, as furnishing a clue to groping Peter, or was it actual necessity which forced that expression? And then, that timid shriek of 'Oh!' as she flies from his extended arms? But still he follows, and she flies not far or fast – and now he grasps her, and bears her boldly under the consecrating Bough, and with unmistakable ardour avails himself of its licence: and I – as her historian – should be sorry to be sworn to say, that Mrs Drodge did her best to elude the pursuit of Peter Batt, or that she resisted his steps towards the mistletoe, or found his salutation so distasteful that its repetition would have angered her. – Our hero was otherwise persuaded, and with reason, since at that very Christmas twelvemonth the village witnessed the nuptials of Peter Batt and Sarah Drodge.

Good reader, as in many a drama of more thrilling interest than the lives and loves of Peter and Sally Batt, it has been the scribe's prerogative to foreclose a tedious current of petty incident, unmarked by any special interest; so now will we imagine an interval of twenty years in the procession of our story, and raise the curtain upon our humble characters after the experience of a score of married years has, let us hope, made Peter Batt a still wiser and better man.

Peter has by this time become an indispensable requisite to the well-being of the village: he has been an honest and industrious man, and has thriven I should think to his heart's content. Sally retains her place in his affections, which has furthermore been strengthened by six additional ties, all promising and healthy. He has extended his business to great advantage – so much so that he has built himself a new house, with workshops and a range of useful outbuildings. And it is a great satisfaction to Peter to stand at some spot which commands the best view of his property, and think that, so to

speak, he is 'monarch of all he surveys'. Yet – as no mortal pilgrimage is ever purely bright – the brow of happy Peter was sometimes beclouded with care: even *his* heart had its vexations – and as his musical genius was instrumental to his discomforts, it will be necessary to make some explanation thereupon.

That 'Woman is fickle' is either a currently-reported fable or a melancholy truism; and though an angel is she in the hour of anguish, yet in the unafflicted moments of her lordly companion doth she too often derive delight in the proof of his subjugation and pleasure in his perplexity. One of Mrs Batt's first demonstrations of displeasure was directed at Peter's much-beloved bassoon, against which, as Mrs Drodge, she had never breathed a syllable to indicate indifference, much less dislike. It was the source of unfeigned consolation to Peter – his bassoon – and she knew it: was she jealous of his having a second bosom-comforter, when the church had put that matter exclusively into her hands? Then, to be sure, he did sacrifice much time to it – time to which Mrs Batt may have thought that holy marriage had entitled *her*, and not 'a plaguey bassoon', as she was wont in hasty moments to designate that respectable instrument. Now, independently of its conveying a sense of comfort to the ear and breast of Peter, his execution of certain pieces with which his bassoon and his neighbours were become familiar, had long secured the latters' compliments, and had also fired the sons of three of them with the noble zeal of emulation. Could Peter forgo with resignation the source of so much pleasure? above all, could he with fortitude relinquish 'the inoffensive manna of soul-sweetening praise?' But Mrs Batt kept up the tune of persecution with wondrous vigor and with weighty argument. 'What,' she would like to know from Peter, 'what would Mrs Cinnamon, the grocer's wife, say of Mr C. if he left her at the church-door on Sundays, to go and join a lot of men and boys?

– Would Mrs Sweetbread (the butcher's better-half), allow her husband to "beneath" himself and treat *her* in such a manner? – She only wanted Peter to speak his mind out, and answer her:' but alas! he, good man, was no match for his wife in volubility, and he therefore dealt with the case in general terms: – 'he wasn't going to *argufy*, nor he wasn't going to be put off from playin'.' This was the position which Peter took up at the beginning of the war, and which he stoutly maintained for a time against the sharp-shooting of the enemy; but as in a wordy engagement with wives few men may hope to triumph, so Peter begun at last to shrink from the incessant and raking fire of his spouse; and the result was, that he compromised his dignity as a man to his affection for his instrument, and did, stealthily and away from home, that which he had not courage left to do there. And this was much to be regretted; for upon such occasions Peter was apt to resort to the 'John Barleycorn', where, privately sore at his humiliation, he would assume considerable boldness – defy 'th' old 'ooman' (meaning Mrs Batt) – and walk off with a fixed determination to do great things at home in reference to his bassoon, which, however, on arriving there, and yielding to second-thoughts, he was always induced to defer.

Never shone the moon more brightly than on the Christmas-eve of 18 – . Never, on any previous occasion, had so much interest been felt as on that auspicious evening, when the good people of the village were surprised in the arms of Morpheus by 'Hark, the herald angels sing!' in original music, composed expressly for the words, by Peter Batt! Yes, Peter had marched forwards; – spite of all opposition and interference, Peter had become a composer. He felt that he was a musician in his heart. We have not space to enter on a critical review of this emanation of his genius, but be assured that all he could do had been done. For some time had he, in kind

compliance with Sarah's wishes, forsaken the instrument on which he had been wont to luxuriate; but as the river, when checked, only gathers an increased force, so did his musical genius burst forth in a written composition, which, as it was produced noiselessly and at home, did not excite the observation of his partner. No sooner was it finished than that 'plaguey bassoon' became in constant use; and for six weeks did the choir of the village church, under the superintendence of our hero, practice what he called 'a Christmas Hymn of my own composin' '. It was highly successful, and report soon spread our author's fame. Rival choirs tried to procure copies, but in vain. At length arrived the longed-for night, on which the public were to have their ears regaled with this splendid production. Big with importance, Peter again took up his bassoon, and at the time appointed boldly sallied forth to meet his friends. Before he left his home, a few hints relative to that 'plaguey bassoon' had slightly ruffled his temper; but two or three glasses of punch at the Barleycorn, the rendezvous of the party, dispelled his gloom, and after one trial he felt reassured and animated, and 'was himself again'. At twelve o'clock behold our party issuing forth in the full confidence of meriting the approbation of all those Christians who like to be disturbed from their comfortable slumbers on Christmas-eve. The success of our hero was beyond all precedent – so much gratified were the villagers that many of them rose, protruded their nightcaps, and prayed for it again. The churchwardens had always made a point of having 'something hot' ready for the 'quire' on its arrival at their respective houses. Now both the churchwardens were Peter's particular friends, and a wee drop extra was prepared for him; and with it came that applause so sweet to an author's ear, that our hero, between the cheering cup and acclamations of his friends, positively forgot himself, and by the time the choral party began to wend its way homewards, Peter Batt was in a very elevated

and unusual state: – I blush to own it, but Peter was decidedly drunk! Alas

> — that men should put an enemy
> Into their mouths to steal away their brains!

Thus it was that Peter fell; yes, reader, he fell morally – aye, and he fell physically too; and two men were obliged to support to his home the author of 'A Christmas Hymn of his own composin' '. Behold him – now shouting, then hallooing – now severely remonstrating with a non-present Mrs Batt on her abuse of his bassoon; and now attempting to convince his two supporters of his superiority on that delightful instrument. Totally unconscious of where he was, the poor composer was left at his own door, about six o'clock in the morning. Poor Sarah had gone to bed at the usual hour, in sad despair at this new outbreak; she could not sleep – she was too anxious for her husband to allow of that; she lay listening to their singing until the sound was lost in the distance; and ever and anon she would fancy she heard them returning, and she would leave her bed and look out on the cold, yet bright moonlight, and wish for his return: thus did she pass a restless night, until she saw with pain the state in which he was brought home. She immediately went down stairs, and with immense difficulty contrived to get Peter *up*, and into bed, though perfectly senseless, and overcome with excitement and strong drink. As soon as she had thus disposed of him, she left, to proceed with the numerous duties which devolve on a mother of six children, especially in preparing a seasonable family banquet for Christmas-day: once or twice she took a candle and crept to the room to ascertain if he was still asleep and comfortable. On the third visit she began to perceive that the sun shining through the curtains was unpleasant to him, as he turned round immediately from it. She remedied the

difficulty by fastening a blanket doubled across the window to keep out the light; and while she was doing so a scheme occurred to her suddenly which she instantly determined to carry out. There Peter lay, snoring and dreaming, in a condition of sottish clairvoyance: now he fancied the sun was glittering on all nature; and he saw the trees studded, as it were, with myriads of diamonds – the effect of the preceding night's frost; and then he saw his own wife and all the children dressed in their best, hastening away to the church; and then they met their neighbours, and the greetings were mutual and satisfactory; and he heard, as he had done for nearly fifty years before, the chime of the village-bells, and he recognized the peal of Christmas-day, and his heart leapt. – But when he tried to jump up and join the pleasant groups he saw, he could not; he had lost all power of motion, and (as he one day confessed to Davy Butler, in confidence), he 'laid like a thinkin' statty'. Then came another season of thick mist upon his senses, and he fancied that he heard 'the herald angels' singing the hymn 'of his own composin' ': then came a volley of applause from listening mortals, which Peter took in greedily – particularly what Davy Butler had said at the church-warden's, that 'there was nor another such a genus that way as Mr Batt, as *he* cou'd hear on in these'em parts'. Then followed a momentary clearance of the fog which hung upon his faculties, and he lifted his leaden head from the pillow, and peered through the parting curtains into perfect and unrelieved darkness, while all was silent as night. Then again he pillowed his aching head, and in a few minutes another phantasmagoria flitted before his distempered mind: now he thought himself in church, but whereabouts he could not well make out; – there was the good old rector, and there his friend the clerk; there also was the choir – but where was himself, Peter Batt? Straining the socket of his mind's eye in order to discover *that* essential, an indescribable figure now fills and now vacates his

place, clutching a huge bassoon: now it rolls backward and forward – now its eyes gleam – now it attempts to carry to its waiting jaw the reed of its bassoon – now after infinite eccentric motions that feat is accomplished, but O! what unearthly noise ensues! – and yes, evidently the bassoonist is drunk, utterly drunk, and in church too! Oh, sin! Oh, shame!

The night appeared long and dreary to Peter, and he looked wistfully towards the window, and longed for some token that it were day: at length his eyes were cheered by the morning-light, peeping in at a corner of the lattice, and Peter bestirred himself to rise. To inspect and remove the strange covering from the window was his first business, and it begun to renew in him an uncomfortable state of feeling. Then the appearance of his clothes was horrifying to his sense of propriety, conveying to his mind the idea of Peter Batt – decent and respectable Peter Batt, in shameful prostration of soul and body. Furthermore, a crowning indignity, as penitent Peter felt it, he had now to endure – and he felt too that it must be endured speechlessly – *the* button had been severed from his coat, by hands in which, morally, he foresaw that he, Peter, must henceforth be mute and passive. His wife, who had been watching his bewilderment, was secretly rejoicing at it, for she foresaw in his confusion and chagrin the perfect success of her scheme. This became the more evident to her when she witnessed Peter's amazement and additional mortification on hearing that he had actually *lost Christmas-day*, and had now awakened on the festival of St Stephen, or the twenty-sixth of December! Reader, my tale is ended. Peter became a more discreet, if not a better man; and I trust many an amateur may learn from his example, that the true source of gratification lies rather in 'the use than in the abuse of art'.

Christmas Tree Poaching

NORMAN GOODLAND AND GILBERT SMITH

The following extracts will strike a chord with all those Hampshire Hogs, for whom 'picking' a Christmas tree from the woods and forests of the county was a traditional and most enjoyable custom of the Season. The first piece from the pen of that notable local writer, Norman Goodland, takes an affectionate look at this local custom. Although entirely fictional, Goodland's story captures the essence of this custom, for both the poacher and the poached, and highlights the seasonal tolerance which has allowed the custom of tree picking to continue.

The night before Christmas Eve, Charlie Roach the keeper stood in the dark passageway behind the bar of the Malt House Inn. The Landlord passed him on his way up from the cellar. He said in a low voice,

''Allo Charlie! Bitter?'

Charlie nodded. The landlord drew it, passed it to him. Charlie paid, without coming into full view of the bar . . .

The landlord went up behind his bar, looked round. Nobody wanted anything he came back.

''Ow's things wi' you then, Charlie? Any trouble?'

'Not lately. I lost a few. Close to Christmas now – should

be alright. Everybody's got whatever they've got. There's always old Amos of course. Is 'e about?'

''E's in there!'

Charlie relaxed. His beer tasted better, knowing where Amos was. He listened. He was used to listening . . .

'I s'pose they cockbirds o' yourn is gone, Amos?'

'Ah! I done-in the last one yest'day!'

'That'll be yourn, then?'

'No.'

'Ha!' said another voice. 'Cain't see old Amos sett'n down to a cockbird for Christmas! 'E'll 'ave summat better'n that!'

'Matter o' fact' said Amos, 'I ain't got nothen in the 'ouse at all!'

'Nothen?'

'Nothen.'

'Cawd – an' you sett'n yere wi' per best cwoat on?'

''E wun't 'ave 'e on b'marnen, I'll be bound!' said another voice.

'Course I shain't! I'll be gwine to work – same as you!'

'Oh ah! Where at?'

'Trimmin' back afore the plough. Up alonzid L-field . . .'

Amos Penfold. A widower. A wiry, cloth capped, jacketed and gaitered man in his late forties. One of the slipperiest poachers Charlie has ever known on his patch. But not a regular – which made him that much more difficult to catch. He usually went poaching when he ran out of casual work. But he could be a nuisance around Christmas time.

Nothing in the house . . .

Charlie thought about that. Might be true. Might be pub talk. Working up around L-field . . .

Charlie thought about that, too. Close to where the birds were bred. And still hung about a bit, in spite of the shooting. H'm . . .

Charlie drank up and quietly left . . .

At half past seven, on the morning of Christmas Eve, Charlie Roach stood – perfectly still – behind the blackthorn at the edge of L-field. He watched a huge concourse above the trees, the rapidly glowing light glinting in their wings. The great flock swung lower, and gradually settled among the stubble.

The tractors had only just started up, down on the farm. Amos would be coming on up before them . . .

He might come straight on up Parnel Lane and in at the gap. He might not . . .

He might make a try, thinking the coast was clear. If he did the flock would certainly warn that somebody was about . . .

He might – like Charlie – be standing in any one of the tall bushes bordering L-field, watching, waiting, making quite sure.

Suddenly a cock pheasant came out from the hedge alongside Parnel Lane. It paused, raised its long neck, looked carefully around. It stopped, did a bit of pretend-feeding. Then it made for the old rick-stump where they had been threshing.

It dropped its wings stiffly, gave them a partridge-like whirr. It called. The call was answered from the lane. A number of other birds appeared, and joined it . . .

Then things began to happen . . .

The lapwings, with a great clamour of high-pitched voices, rose from the flock in the field in a huge, flickering, black and white swirl. The gulls stayed down but were nervous; a few of the younger ones rose with the lapwings. Only the starlings as if used to all this pother, took not notice of it all.

Gradually the frightened plovers returned to the stubble. Silent once more – but watchful. Charlie looked across at the pheasants. His practised eye could just distinguish them, now frozen to the earth like clods.

That was the place to watch! If Amos was going to make his try – it would be there . . .

But it was puzzling, – that disturbance! It was the kind of

demonstration you'd expect when danger – might be more remote . . . Charlie did not think Amos would be the cause of that. He'd have seen the flock settle down into L-field in the first place. He wouldn't have done anything to disturb them – and so give himself away.

The pheasants were on the move again. Scratching like hens in the chaff and the cavings.

Suddenly, the plovers again clamoured, and again rose into the air. The pheasants once more vanished to the ground. It seemed that the whole cycle of events was to be repeated . . .

Then Charlie found himself in the midst of a host of tiny birds. Blue-tits, great-tits, chaffinches, linnets, all passing through the blackthorns and bushes about him, with tiny alarmed cries . . . But these were from the fir plantation! Amos wouldn't be there. And even if he was he wouldn't cause this commotion!

Then it dawned on Charlie. Somebody in the plantation – after the Christmas trees.

All thoughts of Amos gone, Charlie turned and hurried towards this more urgent business! And no sooner had he left his post than there was a furtive movement from behind the rick-stump. A net was cast, and the birds were taken, even as they sat frozen to the ground!

Charlie hurried softly along the drive. As he got nearer to the plantation, he stood still to listen.

He heard a boy's voice, clear as a bell. He recognized it! If it wasn't young Jim, the image of his father Amos in his walk and ways. Who like Amos, always crossed to the other side of the road when he saw Charlie, and passed by with his head down and that infuriating, sly grin.

Charlie boiled. Father pinching the birds – and the kids pinching the trees! High time, he reckoned, this family was cleared off the estate. A conviction for pinching Christmas trees would go a long way towards that!

Charlie pressed grimly on. He followed the boundary netting

towards the sound. Yes – it was Jim alright – and the whole blooming brood. Young Stanley, Marjorie and the two five year olds, Thurza and John! All gathered around that young devil Jim, who was peeling off his gloves as if he meant business.

Charlie waited. A few cuts into the tree wouldn't hurt and you had to get evidence.

The older girl said excitedly,

'Bet you cain't do it in one hit, Jim!'

'Don't be daft Marg! Course I cain't! But I'll do it in six! Stand back! Keep they twins out of the way! ready?'

'One' shouted Marjorie and young Stanley together 'TWO! THREE . . .' The boy missed the next blow and the axe twirled from his grasp and landed in the nearby bushes, and they all laughed. He went to retrieve it. And that was when Charlie advanced upon them.

Five pairs of startled eyes turned towards him. Four mouths sagged with fear but not young Jim's! *He* left the axe where it lay, he was going to blazon it out!

The girl Marjorie turned to run away. Jim called sharply,

'Come back there Marj! No need to run away. We ain't done nothink.'

The boy faced up to Charlie.

'We'm only looking out for a bit of firewood, Mr Roach!'

'Firewood boy? D'you gen'lly chop down green trees for firewood?'

The boy put on an air of injured innocence.

'Well we was lookin' at this yere tree – but we never done that! D'you know that, Mister. We reckons somebody been up here tryin' to steal un for Christmas! But we never'ad nothink to do wi' it I'd swear to that anywheres.'

Charlie walked over to the bush where the axe lay, pulled it out and said 'Well boy – swear to that!'

The boy was still trying.

'That ain't nothink to do wi'we, Mister!'

Charlie said "'Tis no good Jim! I stood there a-watching ye! I zid ye cut the tree!'

The boy's courage evaporated, and he stood there wretchedly.

There was a twinge at Charlie's heart. Only a nipper! And a good, hard try . . .

But he said 'Right-ho! Clutter-off home the lot on' ye! You'd best tell your father what's happened. 'E'll 'ave to know when the P'liceman comes!'

The boy hadn't quite given up.

'Can I have my axe Mister?'

'You knows you cain't 'ave your axe, boy. If you took un from your father wi'out 'is knowin' – they might give un back to un – when you have been convicted! And punished!'

The lad led the subdued, miserable little crowd outside the compound. Charlie watched them go . . .

Somehow, he felt no satisfaction at what he had done. Something was speaking to him – a voice not always the best thing to listen to, for a Keeper! It was a voice called conscience. It reminded him of the struggle a widower might have being left with that tribe of children . . . How it might be all the harder if that widower depended on casual work for a living . . . How if they got turned off the estate, they'd have a job to find anywhere. And them kids might end up in the Workhouse. And all started at Christmas time. And what would folk think about that . . . ?

And the voice said again, that Amos generally only poached when he'd run out of casual work . . . And was only a nuisance at Christmas-time . . .

Charlie suddenly said, 'Come on back yere. Come on back – the lot of ye . . .'

'Now' he said as they trailed back towards him. 'You cain't 'ave this yere tree 'cause 'e's growed for timber – not for Christmas tree! 'E's too big. You come along wi' me – and I'll show you thee one you can 'ave.'

The miserable little faces were transformed with relief and delight.

'Thanks very much, Mister!' said the ever ready Jim.

'I'll thank thee very much! You be gwine t' grow-up as cunnin' as a diddicoi – you be! You'm pretty near 'alf a one now!'

He led them to the edge of the compound.

'Now then this yer tree is stunted and got a kink in un, cause 'e's on the edge o' compound and d'catch the wind! You can 'ave 'e – 'e wun't make good timber! Now you clutter-off down the drive there, Jim – and you'll find my spade under the lean-to besides my little hut!'

'Be you gwine to dig 'im up Mister?'

'That's what I'm gwine to do. Then you plant 'im in the garden wi' a bit o' sacking around the roots – and use 'im every year! Then you won't 'ave to come up botherin' me no more.'

The boy ran off. Charlie stood there still trying to look stern. The boy returned with the spade. Charlie handed him the axe and told him he'd no business to have it. Then he dug out the tree and stood it aside.

'There you are! Now you can see – that's jes the right height!'

They all looked up at it with eyes which had already dressed it with streamers and stars and silver bells and candles and a fairy on the top. Charlie permitted himself a smile.

'Well you cain't carry the axe and the tree as well', he said to Jim, 'And 'tis too heavy for young Marj here. I'll bring it down far thee!'

He swung the tree upon his shoulder, and they trailed out of the drive and down the lane behind him.

When Charlie reached Amos' cottage, he was in a jovial mood. But who should be coming up the lane towards him than the poacher himself?

He looked worried.

'What's on then, Keeper?'

'Mr Roach, he brought us down a Christmas tree – and dug it up hisself!' said Marjorie. 'Wasn't that kind of 'im Dad?'

Amos gave a nervous hitch to his coat.

'You looks as if you'm putting on weight, Amos!' observed Charlie.

'You'll ha' to do something about it! Else you won't be able to move fast enough, will 'e?'

Amos didn't answer. It wasn't time to push his luck.

His mood changed, Charlie felt a sudden feeling of warmth towards Amos.

'Look,' he said 'Why don't you clutter-off on to 'Is Lardship's Estate – and leave my stuff alone? I'll be bound to catch thee sooner or later! I near as dang-it coped thee up in L-field this mornin'.'

And Amos stood there with his coat all loose and heavy around him and said,

'L-field? I ain't been near the place.'

Charlie felt his mood change again. He threw down the tree and walked away . . .

He knew what Amos had under his coat . . .

He fell to thinking of the conversation in the pub . . .

'Cain't see old Amos sett'n down to a cockbird for Christmas . . . !'

And then – that voice that he ought not to listen to if he was going to do a proper job, spoke to him again. And it said, 'Well Charlie Roach! What will you be sett'n down to . . . ?'

The second extract, which takes rather a different view of Christmas tree poaching, comes from the memoirs of Gilbert Smith.

A Hampshire Christmas

*Born in 1922, the son of a New Forest keeper, Smith grew
up in an environment which commanded his deep respect.*

*Following in his father's footsteps he became, firstly, beat
keeper at Ashurst and later the head keeper at Stoney Cross.*

*During this career as a keeper Smith encountered several
locals helping themselves to Christmas trees, and his concern at
what is, after all, an entirely unfriendly custom in
environmental terms, is obvious from the extract below.*

As any keeper in the New Forest, I was to learn over the years
quite a lot about the wildlife and also a lot about human nature
and I had not been about my job long before I became aware that
there were so many unsavoury characters who came and abused
the Forest in many ways and I would not have been doing a good
job if I had allowed their nasty habits to go unchecked and I
went to great pains to make sure that they didn't come back to
my patch too often, once I had apprehended them.

It may not be the worst crime in the book, but people who
came to help themselves to Christmas trees were somewhat of
an irritation to me. I remember the first time I came across a
fellow in a plantation just before Christmas. I watched him
while he pulled and tugged the young tree this way and then
that. He was having some difficulty in getting it up and had
his back to me, so did not hear me quietly walk towards him.
He jumped clean over the tree in fright when I said 'What
might you be doing?'

I was to learn from this incident, as in court this case was
dismissed as the fellow had not actually taken a tree. The fact
that he had tried hard did not cut any ice. In future I made
sure that I waited quite long enough for everyone at the same
game to have the tree in his hand after that!

No, I did not much like people who took trees and I am

sure they didn't much like me, either, but you were in the wrong job, keepering, if you were out for popularity stakes. Another Christmas-tree incident was a couple who arrived on bicycles which they promptly hid in some bushes. I had a notion what they were after, so when they were safely out of sight, I moved the cycles and pushed them some ways away. I waited in the trees and it was not long before I heard the couple coming back and, yes, sure enough they were carrying two sawn-off trees. They had found them beside the road, they said, but the saw was eventually produced from the man's pocket and they gave me names and addresses. Off I went on my rounds, not waiting to see if they found their cycles. I checked on that the next morning and, sure enough the cycles were still where I had left them. My next call was Totton to verify the names and addresses I had been given, but no-one had heard of them, not even the Police.

It was only a matter of time before the couple reported their bikes stolen. They had, they said, gone out into the Forest for a walk and when they returned, their cycles had disappeared. The Police, of course, contacted me and they got their cycles back, plus a fine for stealing the trees, and another for supplying false names and addresses.

Yes, there were quite a few people out after trees and there were lots of different reactions when they were discovered, like the one who was instantly sick – I must have had a weak moment, for I took pity on him and did not pursue the matter. Some tried bribery and one pretended he couldn't speak English – until he tried to start his car and found it would not go.

'What have you done to my car?' he said. 'Oh,' I said, 'you do speak English after all. Well perhaps you'll understand this – we're taking a trip to Lyndhurst Police Station – I'm coming with you, when I've put the necessary bit back on the car.'

Taking out the rotor arms of vehicles was a thing I did several times but once it left me with a bit of a guilty conscience.

One moonlight night I went to Deerleep at Christmas-tree time and saw a lorry backed off the main road and about one hundred yards from the plantation. No-one was with it so I made a note of the number and, as was my usual drill, concealed the paper in my sock where only my wife would know where to find it should anything go wrong any time. Then I removed the rotor arm.

'Good job I spotted this,' I thought, 'otherwise goodness knows how many trees would have gone tonight.'

The night was still but cold and the moon had moved some way before a second lorry came along and backed up to the first. I could hear voices and saw some movement of two, perhaps three men. Then the next thing I knew, the second lorry started up and towed the first one away. It just had not occurred to me that the first lorry had broken down, I had jumped to the wrong conclusion. I just stood there, dumbfounded, unable to do anything about it. I often wondered what was said when they found the rotor arm missing.

The Cadnam Oak

GILPIN

One of the most intriguing legends of the New Forest is almost as old as the ancient woodland itself and is just part of the mystery and speculation which surrounds the accidental death (or was it murder?) of William Rufus, the son of

William I, who is credited with creating the Forest as his own personal hunting ground.

According to the legend Rufus was out hunting when he was hit by an arrow which bounced off a nearby oak tree. One Sir Walter Tyrrel was subsequently accused of murdering the king, but whether his actions were deliberate or a freak accident has never been resolved.

Charles II is said to have constructed a paling around the oak tree which deflected the arrow and, like the Glastonbury Thorn, locals reported that the tree defied nature by budding every year on Christmas Day. When the oak died of sheer old age in the middle of the eighteenth century, Walter Delaware had a monument erected in its place called the Rufus Stone.

This was not the last of the legend. Locals took cuttings from the original oak and planted them at Copythorne, where a tree called the Cadnam Oak is said to have grown with the same miraculous properties as the original.

Parties were held beneath the branches of Cadnam Oak on Christmas Eve and people took cuttings from the tree in the hope that they would take root elsewhere.

The tree's fame obviously reached the historian Gilpin, who decided to investigate its properties and reports them in his book Forest Scenery, *first published in 1791. His scepticism is very apparent, but his conclusion that the tree budded on 'Old Christmas Day', refusing to acknowledge the calendar changes of 1752, is an interesting one.*

The last celebrated tree, which I shall present to the reader from New-forest, is the Cadenham oak, which buds every year

The Cadnam Oak?

in the depth of winter. Cadenham is a village, about three miles from Lyndhurst on the Salisbury road.

Having often heard of this oak, I took a ride to see it on the 29th of december 1781. It was pointed out to me among several other oaks, surrounded by a little forest stream, winding round a knoll, on which they stood. It is a tall, straight plant of no great age, and apparently vigorous; except that it's top has been injured; from which several branches issue in the form of pollard shoots. It was intirely bare of leaves, as far as I could discern, when I saw it; and undistinguishable from the other oaks in its neighbourhood; except that its bark seemed rather smoother; occasioned, I apprehended, only by frequent climbing.

Having had the account of its *early budding* confirmed on the spot, I engaged one Michael Lawrence, who kept the White Hart, a small ale house in the neighbourhood, to send

me some of the leaves to Vicar's hill, as soon as they should appear. The man, who had not the least doubt about the matter, kept his word; and sent me several twigs, on the morning of the 5th of january 1782; a few hours after they had been gathered. The leaves were fairly expanded; and about an inch in length. From some of the buds two leaves had unsheathed themselves; but in general only one.

Through what power in nature this strange, premature vegetation is occasioned, I believe no naturalist can explain. I sent some of the leaves to one of the ablest botanists we have, Mr Lightfoot, author of the *Flora Scotica*; and was in hopes of hearing something satisfactory on the subject. But he is one of those philosophers, who is not ashamed of ignorance, where attempts at knowledge are mere conjecture. He assured me, that he neither could account for it in any way; nor did he know of any other instance of premature vegetation, except the Glastonbury-thorn.

The *philosophers of the forest*, in the meantime, account for the thing at once, through the influence of old Christmas-day; universally believing that the oak buds on that day, and that only. The same opinion is held with regard to the Glastonbury-thorn by the common people of the west of England. But without doubt, the germination there is gradual; and forwarded, or retarded by the mildness, or severity of the weather. One of it's progeny, which grew in the gardens of the duchess dowager of Portland, at Bulstrode, had its flower-buds perfectly formed, so early, as the 21st of december 1781; which is fifteen days earlier than it ought to flower, according to the vulgar prejudice*.

* In the *Salisbury journal* january 10th 1786, the following paragraph appeared.

> In consequence of a report, that has prevailed in this country for upwards of two centuries, and which by many has been almost considered as a matter of faith, that the oak at Cadenham, in the

New-forest, shoots forth leaves on every old Christmas-day, and that no leaf is ever to be seen on it, either before, or after that day, during the winter; a lady, who is now on a visit in this city, and who is attentively curious in everything relative to art or nature, made a journey to Cadenham on monday the 3rd instant, purposely to enquire, on the spot, about the production of this famous tree. On her arrival near it, the usual guide was ready to attend her; but on his being desired to climb the oak, and to search whether there were any leaves then on it, he said it would be to no purpose, but that if she would come on the wednesday following (Christmas-day) she might certainly see thousands. However he was prevailed on to ascend, and on the first branch which he gathered, appeared several fair new leaves, fresh sprouted from the buds, and nearly an inch and a half in length. It may be imagined, that the guide was more amazed at this premature production than the lady; for so strong was his belief in the truth of the whole tradition, that he would have pledged his life, that not a leaf was to have been discovered on any part of the tree before the usual hour.

But tho the superstitious part of this ancient legend is hence confuted, yet it must be allowed that there is something very uncommon and curious in an oak's constantly shooting forth leaves at this unseasonable time of the year, and that the cause of it well deserves the philosophical attention of the botanist. In some years there is no doubt that this oak may shew it's *first* leaves on the Christmas morning, as probably as on a few days before; and this perhaps was the case in the last year, when a gentleman of this neighbourhood, a nice and critical observer, strictly examined the branches, not only on the Christmas morn, but also on the day prior to it. On the first day not a leaf was to be found, but on the following every branch had its complement, tho they were then but just shooting from the buds, none of them being more than a quarter of an inch long. The latter part of the story may easily be credited, that no leaves are to be seen on it after Christmas-day, as large parties yearly assemble about the oak on that morning, and regularly strip every appearance of a leaf from it.

This early spring however of the Cadenham oak is of very short duration. The buds, after unfolding themselves, make no farther progress; but immediately shrink from the season, and die. The tree continues torpid, like other deciduous trees,

during the remainder of the winter, and vegetates again in the spring, at the usual season. I have seen it, in full leaf, in the middle of summer, when it appeared both in its form, and foliage, exactly like other oaks.

I have been informed, that another tree with the same property of early germination, has lately been found near the spot, where Rufus's monument stands. If this be the case, it seems, in some degree to authenticate the account which Camden gives us of the scene of that prince's death: for he speaks of the premature vegetation of that very tree, on which the arrow of Tyrrel glanced; and the tree I now speak of, if it really exists, tho I have no sufficient authority for it, might have been a descendant of the old oak, and have inherited its virtues.

It is very probable however there may be other oaks in the forest, which may likewise have the property of early germination. I have heard it often suspected, that people gather buds from other trees, and carry them, on old Christmas-day, to the oak at Cadenham, from whence they pretended to pluck them. For that tree is in such repute; and resorted to annually by so many visitants, that I think it could not easily supply all its votaries, without some foreign contributions. – Some have accounted for this phenomenon by supposing that leaves have been preserved over the year by being steeped in vinegar. But I am well satisfied this is not the case. Mr Lightfoot, to whom I sent the leaves, had no such suspicion.

from

A New Forest Commoner Remembers . . .

HUGH PASMORE

Born in 1908 in nearby Southampton, Hugh Pasmore spent over sixty years of his life living and working in the New Forest. His decision to write a book about his life as a New Forest Commoner came, he says, 'When . . . I achieved four score years and was no longer capable of taking part in active Forest life, I felt I should put on paper some of the stories told me by the foresters and commoners, together with extracts from a monthly column I wrote over a period of 18 years for four Forest newspapers.'

Although a chartered surveyor by profession, Pasmore's knowledge and love of the Forest provide compelling tales of rescuing drowning ponies from bogs, being beaten up by deer poachers, walking the entire ninety-mile boundary of the Forest and this tale, which recounts one of the New Forest's most popular Christmas traditions.

Boxing Day Point-to-Point Races

One of the highlights of the Forest Commoner's year is the Boxing Day point-to-point races across three miles of open Forest.

The course is set by a local Commoner, usually one who has himself competed in his earlier days, and is designed to test horse and rider to the full. Bogs, thick woodland and other hazards form part of every course and at the finish there are a lot of weary riders and ponies.

Competitors are told, a month or so before the race, the area of the finish but, so that no practising can take place, no indication as to the starting point is given. In fact the start can be anywhere within a 360 degree circle provided it is three miles in distance.

The first of these point-to-points was held on Boxing Day in 1911 when the course was from Millyford to Ocknell and the race was won by Lord Lucas. The original cup was eventually won outright after three successive victories by Frank Shutler.

Nowadays there are several races: in addition to the Commoners' races there are two children's races, a ladies' race, an open race and a veterans' race. In addition to the stewards at the start and finish, a 'riding steward' accompanies both of the children's races – a role which can have its perils.

All the races are exciting, especially to the competitors, and some finishes can be extremely close, despite the three-mile course. The events I have described below are derived from personal experience, but undoubtedly other riders can relate adventures equally, if not more exciting.

Never Too Old

The 1967 New Forest Boxing Day races took place in ideal weather finishing on the old aerodrome at Beaulieu.

Once again great interest centred on the Veterans' race which had entrants aged sixty and above. Incredibly the oldest competitor, Jim Whitehorn of Bramshaw, was almost eighty-one. A week before the race a discussion took place in the Bell Inn at Brook, where I was astounded to hear this remark: 'Trouble with old Jim is that he can't see, but I have told him to keep right on my tail until the finishing straight and then he can have a go!'

As it turned out Jim needed no one to follow, for he led right up to the last hundred yards, when seventy-five-year-old Ted Burry, on his thoroughbred, managed to scrape a win by a narrow margin.

A Hair-Raising Point-to-Point

The 1968 point-to-point was held on Easter Saturday (postponed from Boxing Day), the start being at Thorney Hill with the finish on Burley Rocks, the distance being the usual three miles.

The course was fast, being across open country but the undulating ground soon sorted out competitors and most finished well strung out. My role was riding steward accompanying children under seventeen on their race.

Having seen them race in many previous years I knew full well what this entailed, for they know only one speed – full gallop! The race started at Holmsley Lodge (children's races cover only $1^1/_2$ miles) and away went the competitors like a flash.

My horse had obviously not read the race card for instead of keeping a decorous 30 yards or so behind, as befits a riding steward, he was quite determined to lead the field. By a supreme effort I managed at least to keep just in the rear though I felt I was fighting a losing battle. As we thundered over Greenberry Bridge, I noticed one competitor streaking

Point-to-point racing on Boxing Day

up the hill to the right on a completely wrong course and could only surmise that he also was out of control.

A few hundred yards past the bridge the rough track turns abruptly across a bog via a narrow path and bridge. The first two riders made it unscathed, but the momentum of the next veered him off the track and down he came.

Immediately on his heels and travelling equally fast, were two girls. I had a fleeting glimpse of both ponies and riders crashing over the faller and three bodies and three ponies appeared inextricably mixed, with the riders seeming to be underneath their mounts. My horse slithered to a standstill as a fourth riderless pony (belonging to the competitor who had taken the wrong course) shot past and blundered through the melee at my feet.

Within seconds all was disentangled and I made a quick calculation of the number of riderless ponies careering away in the distance and checked that the number of children on their

feet corresponded. Satisfied that all humans appeared reasonably mobile, I set off after the three riderless ponies which were indulging in their own private race. The fourth was plunging through the bog pursued by its owner, who must have required considerable cleaning on arriving home.

On reaching the road my three quarries sped down the verge towards old Holmsley station. At this point a girl in a car shot ahead, jumped out and cleverly grabbed one's rein as they passed, this leaving a grey and a bay still galloping. At the main road grid the bay split off down the side fence, but the grey, harassed by some thoughtless cars behind, went straight over on to the A35.

Knowing the grid was looming up I had slowed down to prevent further frightening the pony, so I don't know whether it jumped or trod the grid but it was a miracle it survived. Luckily one of the Dovey family (well-known Commoners) was passing on his way to the finish, and he soon had the grey quietened, whilst the bay returned of its own accord and stood close to the grey but on the Forest side of the fence.

Thus all ended well and I led the culprits back across the moor to meet up with the two owners tramping across the heather.

That evening I made a note in my diary: 'Next year I think I will enter the open race – it will be quieter.'

Children's Races: Fraught with Difficulties

In 1972 I was entrusted with the job of setting the course for the point-to-point races since there is not much country in the north of the Forest which I don't know intimately.

I spent much time trying to devise a course which would cause competitors to scratch their heads as to the best route to follow. The fact that ultimately riders merged from four separate directions made me feel I had succeeded.

My daughter and I were detailed to ride with the competitors in the second of the children's races, in case of accidents, and we started from the Sloden end of Hasley Inclosure. It is traditional in these races that if you come from the other side of the Forest and don't know the territory, you have little to worry about, for you merely follow one of the local competitors until the finish looms in sight and then you go for it.

Alas, this year this plan went astray, for none of the competing children knew the lay of the country. Hard-heartedly, I refused to enlighten them. The first children's race went off with Pirette Mangin in attendance in case of mishaps; five minutes later, I started the second race, with the children setting off at a spanking gallop.

At the end of Hasley Inclosure, the riders cut across the heath for Linwood and the correct line to the finish. It was here that we encountered a disconsolate Miss Mangin who told us that her riders had turned right, going round the Inclosure on a route leading directly back to the starting line!

Our job was to keep with our competitors, so we swept on regardless. It was only when we reached the Linwood Ford that I glanced over my shoulder and saw Race No. 1, which had discovered its mistake, racing madly along in the wake of No. 2, a good five minutes adrift. My daughter and I pulled up clear of the track to allow the contestants to gallop past, while they shouted urgently for directions.

Relenting somewhat, I shouted 'Turn left over the ford!' but by now obviously past caring, the whole lot turned right careering towards Linwood. Only because my daughter and I have extremely loud voices were we able to recall them.

Even so, they were gluttons for punishment, for instead of a direct run up Amberslade to the waiting crowds at the finish, they elected to veer right past High Corner Hotel on to the Linwood Road and thence to the finishing line, nearly doubling the official children's race distance from 1 1/2 miles to

3 miles. One rather pathetic casualty was a small boy who was twice unseated before he even arrived at the start and who we espied displaying his racing number but walking his pony disconsolately.

On being offered assistance he said sadly he thought perhaps he would give up the idea of competing. Four hours later I was telephoned to say he had not been seen since, so I at once set off to tour the Godshill – Frogham area in search of him.

In one of the lanes I found his racing numbers tied to a gate. The occupants had found him wandering, taken him in with his pony, and a phone call had soon brought his anxious parents to the rescue.

from

Emma

JANE AUSTEN

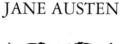

Jane Austen is, of course, one of the most famous personalities that Hampshire can lay claim to. Born in Steventon in December 1775, the daughter of the parish rector, Austen lived in the county for most of her life, only leaving for the occasional visit to London or Bath. Her fictional world of the minor landed gentry, the country clergy, the rural village and the county town is based largely on her observations of life in early nineteenth-century Hampshire.

A Hampshire Christmas

The action in all six of Austen's novels tends to take place in winter, but there are practically no references to Christmas or Christmas Day itself. The outstanding exception occurs in the pages of Emma, *where we are treated to an ill-fated dinner party at the Westons, on Christmas Eve.*

I have included two extracts – the first, which takes place in the carriage on the way to the party will undoubtedly strike a chord with any modern readers for whom the plethora of Christmas parties comes as a great trial.

The second piece occurs afterwards when, emboldened by 'Mr Weston's good wine', Mr Elton has the effrontery to propose to Emma in the coach on the way home.

Emma soon saw that her companion was not in the happiest humour. The preparing and the going abroad in such weather, with the sacrifice of his children after dinner, were evils, were disagreeables at least, which Mr John Knightley did not by any means like; he anticipated nothing in the visit that could be at all worth the purchase; and the whole of their drive to the Vicarage was spent by him in expressing his discontent.

'A man', said he, 'must have a very good opinion of himself when he asks people to leave their own fireside, and encounter such a day as this, for the sake of coming to see him. He must think himself a most agreeable fellow; I could not do such a thing. It is the greatest absurdity – Actually snowing at this moment! – The folly of not allowing people to be comfortable at home – and the folly of people's not staying comfortably at home when they can! If we were obliged to go out such an evening as this, by any call of duty or business, what a hardship we should deem it; – and here are we, probably with rather thinner clothing than usual, setting forward voluntarily, without excuse, in defiance of the voice of nature, which

Jane Austen's former home at Chawton

tells man, in every thing given to his view or his feelings, to stay at home himself, and keep all under shelter that he can; – here are we setting forward to spend five dull hours in another man's house, with nothing to say or to hear that was not said and heard yesterday, and may not be said and heard again to-morrow. Going in dismal weather, to return probably in worse; – four horses and four servants taken out for nothing but to convey five idle, shivering creatures into colder rooms and worse company than they might have had at home.'

Emma did not find herself equal to give the pleased assent, which no doubt he was in the habit of receiving, to emulate the 'Very true, my love,' which must have been usually administered by his travelling companion; but she had resolution enough to refrain from making any answer at all. She could not be complying, she dreaded being quarrelsome; her heroism reached only to silence. She allowed him to talk, and

arranged the glasses, and wrapped herself up, without opening her lips.

They arrived, the carriage turned, the step was let down,
and Mr Elton, spruce, black, and smiling, was with them
instantly. Emma thought with pleasure of some change of
subject. Mr Elton was all obligation and cheerfulness; he was
so very cheerful in his civilities indeed, that she began to
think he must have received a different account of Harriet
from what had reached her. She had sent while dressing, and
the answer had been, 'Much the same – not better.'

'*My* report from Mrs Goddard's', said she presently, 'was
not so pleasant as I had hoped – "Not better," was *my* answer.'

His face lengthened immediately; and his voice was the
voice of sentiment as he answered.

'Oh! no – I am grieved to find – I was on the point of
telling you that when I called at Mrs Goddard's door, which I
did the very last thing before I returned to dress, I was told
that Miss Smith was not better, by no means better, rather
worse. Very much grieved and concerned – I had flattered
myself that she must be better after such a cordial as I knew
had been given in the morning.'

Emma smiled and answered – 'My visit was of use to the
nervous part of her complaint, I hope; but not even I can
charm away a sore throat; it is a most severe cold indeed. Mr
Perry has been with her, as you probably heard.'

'Yes – I imagined – that is – I did not' –

'He has been used to her in these complaints, and I hope
to-morrow morning will bring us both a more comfortable
report. But it is impossible not to feel uneasiness. Such a sad
loss to our party to-day!'

'Dreadful! – Exactly so, indeed. – She will be missed every
moment.'

This was very proper; the sigh which accompanied it was
really estimable; but it should have lasted longer. Emma was

rather in dismay when only half a minute afterwards he began to speak of other things, and in a voice of the greatest alacrity and enjoyment.

'What an excellent device,' said he, 'the use of a sheep-skin for carriages. How very comfortable they make it; – impossible to feel cold with such precautions. The contrivances of modern days indeed have rendered a gentleman's carriage perfectly complete. One is so fenced and guarded from the weather, that not a breath of air can find its way unpermitted. Weather becomes absolutely of no consequence. It is a very cold afternoon – but in this carriage we know nothing of the matter. – Ha! snows a little I see.'

'Yes,' said John Knightley, 'and I think we shall have a good deal of it.'

'Christmas weather,' observed Mr Elton. 'Quite seasonable; and extremely fortunate we may think ourselves that it did not begin yesterday, and prevent this day's party, which it might very possibly have done, for Mr Woodhouse would hardly have ventured had there been much snow on the ground; but now it is of no consequence. This is quite the season indeed for friendly meetings. At Christmas every body invites their friends about them, and people think little of even the worst weather. I was snowed up at a friend's house once for a week. Nothing could be pleasanter. I went for only one night, and could not get away till that very day se'nnight.'

Mr John Knightley looked as if he did not comprehend the pleasure, but said only, coolly.

'I cannot wish to be snowed up a week at Randalls.'

At another time Emma might have been amused, but she was too much astonished now at Mr Elton's spirits for other feelings. Harriet seemed quite forgotton in the expectation of a pleasant party.

'We are sure of excellent fires,' continued he, 'and every

thing in the greatest comfort. Charming people, Mr and Mrs
Weston; – Mrs Weston indeed is much beyond praise, and he
is exactly what one values, so hospitable, and so fond of society; – it will be a small party, but where small parties are
select, they are perhaps the most agreeable of any. Mr
Weston's dining-room does not accommodate more than ten
comfortably; and for my part, I would rather, under such circumstances, fall short by two than exceed by two. I think you
will agree with me (turning with a soft air to Emma), I think
I shall certainly have your approbation, though Mr Knightley
perhaps, from being used to the large parties of London, may
not quite enter into our feelings.'

'I know nothing of the large parties of London, sir – I never
dine with any body.'

'Indeed! (in a tone of wonder and pity), I had no idea that
the law had been so great a slavery. Well, sir, the time must
come when you will be paid for all this, when you will have
little labour and great enjoyment.'

'My first enjoyment,' replied John Knightley, as they
passed through the sweep-gate, 'will be to find myself safe at
Hartfield again.'

The carriages came: and Mr Woodhouse, always the first
object on such occasions, was carefully attended to his own by
Mr Knightley and Mr Weston; but not all that either could
say could prevent some renewal of alarm at the sight of the
snow which had actually fallen, and the discovery of a much
darker night than he had been prepared for. 'He was afraid
they should have a very bad drive. He was afraid poor Isabella
would not like it. And there would be poor Emma in the carriage behind. He did not know what they had best do. They
must keep as much together as they could;' and James was
talked to, and given a charge to go very slow and wait for the
other carriage.

Portrait of Jane Austen by her sister, Cassandra, *c.* 1810

Isabella stept in after her father; John Knightley, forgetting that he did not belong to their party, stept in after his wife very naturally; so that Emma found, on being escorted and followed into the second carriage by Mr Elton, that the door was to be lawfully shut on them, and that they were to have a tête-à-tête drive. It would not have been the awkwardness of a moment, it would have been rather a pleasure, previous to the suspicions of this very day; she could have talked to him of Harriet, and the three-quarters of a mile would have seemed but one. But now, she would rather it had not happened. She believed he had been drinking too much of Mr Weston's good wine, and felt sure that he would want to be talking nonsense.

To restrain him as much as might be, by her own manners, she was immediately preparing to speak with exquisite calmness and gravity of the weather and the night; but scarcely had she begun, scarcely had they passed the sweep-gate and joined the other carriage, than she found her subject cut up –

her hand seized – her attention demanded, and Mr Elton actually making violent love to her: availing himself of the precious opportunity, declaring sentiments which must be already well known, hoping – fearing – adoring – ready to die if she refused him; but flattering himself that his ardent attachment and unequalled love and unexampled passion could not fail of having some effect, and in short, very much resolved on being seriously accepted as soon as possible. It really was so. Without scruple – without apology – without much apparent diffidence, Mr Elton, the lover of Harriet, was professing himself *her* lover. She tried to stop him; but vainly; he would go on, and say it all. Angry as she was, the thought of the moment made her resolve to restrain herself when she did speak. She felt that half this folly must be drunkenness, and therefore could hope that it might belong only to the passing hour. Accordingly, with a mixture of the serious and the playful, which she hoped would best suit his half and half state, she replied,

'I am very much astonished, Mr Elton. This to *me*! you forget yourself – you take me for your friend – any message to Miss Smith I shall be happy to deliver; but no more of this to *me*, if you please.'

'Miss Smith! – Message to Miss Smith! – What could she possibly mean!' – And he repeated her words with such assurance of accent, such boastful pretence of amazement, that she could not help replying with quickness.

'Mr Elton, this is the most extraordinary conduct! and I can account for it only in one way; you are not yourself, or you could not speak either to me, or of Harriet, in such a manner. Command yourself enough to say no more, and I will endeavour to forget it.'

But Mr Elton had only drunk wine enough to elevate his spirits, not at all to confuse his intellects. He perfectly knew his own meaning; and having warmly protested against her

suspicion as most injurious, and slightly touched upon his respect for Miss Smith as her friend, – but acknowledging his wonder that Miss Smith should be mentioned at all, – he resumed the subject of his own passion, and was very urgent for a favourable answer.

As she thought less of his inebriety, she thought more of his inconstancy and presumption; and with fewer struggles for politeness, replied,

'It is impossible for me to doubt any longer. You have made yourself too clear. Mr Elton, my astonishment is much beyond any thing I can express. After such behaviour, as I have witnessed during the last month, to Miss Smith – such attentions as I have been in the daily habit of observing – to be addressing me in this manner – this is an unsteadiness of character, indeed, which I had not supposed possible! Believe me, sir, I am far, very far, from gratified in being the object of such professions.'

'Good heaven!' cried Mr Elton, 'what can be the meaning of this? – Miss Smith! – I never thought of Miss Smith in the whole course of my existence – never paid her any attentions, but as your friend: never cared whether she were dead or alive, but as your friend. If she has fancied otherwise, her own wishes have misled her, and I am very sorry – extremely sorry – But, Miss Smith, indeed! – Oh! Miss Woodhouse! who can think of Miss Smith, when Miss Woodhouse is near! I have thought only of you. I protest against having paid the smallest attention to any one else. Every thing that I have said or done, for many weeks past, has been with the sole view of marking my adoration of yourself. You cannot really, seriously, doubt it. No! – (in an accent meant to be insinuating) – I am sure you have seen and understood me.'

It would be impossible to say what Emma felt, on hearing this – which of all her unpleasant sensations was uppermost. She was too completely overpowered to be immediately able

to reply: and two moments of silence being ample encouragement for Mr Elton's sanguine state of mind, he tried to take her hand again, as he joyously exclaimed –

'Charming Miss Woodhouse! allow me to interpret this interesting silence. It confesses that you have long understood me.'

'No, sir,' cried Emma, 'it confesses no such thing. So far from having long understood you, I have been in a most complete error with respect to your views, till this moment. As to myself, I am very sorry that you should have been giving way to any feelings – Nothing could be farther from my wishes – your attachment to my friend Harriet – your pursuit of her, (pursuit, it appeared) gave me great pleasure, and I have been very earnestly wishing you success: but had I supposed that she were not your attraction to Hartfield, I should certainly have thought you judged ill in making your visits so frequent. Am I to believe that you have never sought to recommend yourself particularly to Miss Smith? – that you have never thought seriously of her?'

'Never, madam,' cried he, affronted, in his turn: 'never, I assure you. I think seriously of Miss Smith! – Miss Smith is a very good sort of girl; and I should be happy to see her respectably settled. I wish her extremely well: and, no doubt, there are men who might not object to – Every body has their level: but as for myself, I am not, I think, quite so much at a loss. I need not so totally despair of an equal alliance, as to be addressing myself to Miss Smith! – No, madam, my visits to Hartfield have been for yourself only; and the encouragement I received' –

'Encouragement! – I give you encouragement! – sir, you have been entirely mistaken in supposing it. I have seen you only as the admirer of my friend. In no other light could you have been more to me than a common acquaintance. I am exceedingly sorry: but it is well that the mistake ends where

it does. Had the same behaviour continued, Miss Smith might have been led into a misconception of your views; not being aware, probably, any more than myself, of the very great inequality which you are so sensible of. But, as it is, the disappointment is single, and, I trust, will not be lasting. I have no thoughts of matrimony at present.'

He was too angry to say another word; her manner too decided to invite supplication; and in this state of swelling resentment, and mutually deep mortification, they had to continue together a few minutes longer, for the fears of Mr Woodhouse had confined them to a foot pace. If there had not been so much anger, there would have been desperate awkwardness; but their straightforward emotions left no room for the little zigzags of embarrassment. Without knowing when the carriage turned into Vicarage-lane, or when it stopped, they found themselves, all at once, at the door of his house; and he was out before another syllable passed. – Emma then felt it indispensable to wish him a good night. The compliment was just returned, coldly and proudly; and, under indescribable irritation of spirits, she was then conveyed to Hartfield.

The Last Chronicle of Barset

ANTHONY TROLLOPE

*Like Thomas Hardy, many nineteenth-century novelists
created an imaginary 'county' where the chapters of their epic
novels could unfold. One such novelist was Anthony Trollope,
who published his first novel in 1847, at the ripe old age of
thirty-two.*

*Although Trollope produced around fifty books he is perhaps
best known for his Barsetshire novels which depict the day-to-
day lives of country and professional people in an imaginary
agricultural area. While many English counties may claim to
be the original 'Barsetshire', there is much evidence to suggest
that Hampshire has the strongest claim of all, and that Barset
itself is a literary version of Winchester.*

*Barsetshire's muddy lanes, rich pastures and comfortable
parsonages are instantly recognizable to the people of Hampshire
as is the following extract, from* The Last Chronicle of
Barset *(1867), where the vicar's wife is proffering more advice
than assistance to two hardworking local women who have
volunteered to decorate the village church for Christmas.*

Down at Allington

It was Christmas-time down at Allington, and at three o'clock on Christmas Eve, just as the darkness of the early winter evening was coming on, Lily Dale and Grace Crawley were seated together, one above the other, on the steps leading up to the pulpit in Allington Church. They had been working all day at the decorations of the church, and they were now looking round them at the result of their handiwork. To an eye unused to the gloom the place would have been nearly dark; but they could see every corner turned by the ivy sprigs, and every line on which the holly-leaves were shining. And the greeneries of the winter had not been stuck up in the old-fashioned, idle way, a bough just fastened up here and a twig inserted there; but everything had been done with some meaning, with some thought towards the original architecture of the building. The Gothic lines had been followed, and all the lower arches which it had been possible to reach with an ordinary ladder had been turned as truly with the laurel cuttings as they had been turned originally with the stone.

'I wouldn't tie another twig,' said the elder girl, 'for all the Christmas pudding that was ever boiled.'

'It's lucky then that there isn't another twig to tie.'

'I don't know about that. I see a score of places where the work has been scamped. This is the sixth time I have done the church, and I don't think I'll ever do it again. When we first began it, Bell and I, you know – before Bell was married, – Mrs Boyce, and the Boycian establishment generally, used to come and help. Or rather we used to help her. Now she hardly ever looks after it at all.'

'She is older, I suppose.'

'She's a little older, and a deal idler. How idle people do get! Look at him. Since he has had a curate he hardly ever stirs round the parish. And he is getting so fat that – H—sh! Here

she is herself, – come to give her judgment upon us.' Then a stout lady, the wife of the vicar, walked slowly up the aisle. 'Well, girls,' she said, 'you have worked hard, and I am sure Mr Boyce will be very much obliged to you.'

'Mr Boyce, indeed! said Lily Dale. 'We shall expect the whole parish to rise from their seats and thank us. Why didn't Jane and Bessy come and help us.'

'They were so tired when they came in from the coal club. Besides, they don't care for this kind of thing, – not as you do.'

'Jane is utilitarian to the backbone, I know,' said Lily, 'and Bessy doesn't like getting up ladders.'

'As for ladders,' said Mrs Boyce, defending her daughter, 'I am not quite sure that Bessy isn't right. You don't mean to say that you did all those capitals yourself?'

'Every twig, with Hopkins to hold the ladder and cut the sticks; and as Hopkins is just a hundred and one years old, we could have done it pretty nearly as well alone.'

'I do not think that,' said Grace.

'He has been grumbling all the time,' said Lily, 'and swears he never will have the laurels so robbed again. Five or six years ago he used to declare that death would certainly save him from the pain of such another desecration before the next Christmas; but he has given up that foolish notion now, and talks as though he meant to protect the Allington shrubs at any rate to the end of this century.'

'I am sure we gave our share from the parsonage,' said Mrs Boyce, who never understood a joke.

'All the best came from the parsonage, as of course they ought,' said Lily. 'But Hopkins had to make up the deficiency. And as my uncle told him to take the haycart for them instead of the hand-barrow, he is broken-hearted.'

'I am sure he was very good-natured,' said Grace.

'Nevertheless he is broken-hearted; and I am very

good-natured too, and I am broken-backed. Who is going to preach to-morrow morning, Mrs Boyce?'

'Mr Swanton will preach in the morning.'

'Tell him not to be long, because of the children's pudding. Tell Mr Boyce if he is long, we won't any of us come next Sunday.'

'My dear, how can you say such wicked things! I shall not tell him anything of the kind.'

'That's not wicked, Mrs Boyce. If I were to say I had eaten so much lunch that I didn't want any dinner, you'd understand that. If Mr Swanton will preach for three-quarters of an hour—'

'He only preached for three-quarters of an hour once, Lily.'

'He has been over the half-hour every Sunday since he has been here. His average is over forty minutes, and I say it's a shame.'

'It is not a shame at all, Lily,' said Mrs Boyce, becoming very serious.

'Look at my uncle; he doesn't like to go to sleep, and he has to suffer a purgatory in keeping himself awake.'

'If your uncle is heavy, how can Mr Swanton help it? If Mr Dale's mind were on the subject he would not sleep.'

'Come, Mrs Boyce; there's somebody else sleeps sometimes besides my uncle. When Mr Boyce puts up his finger and just touches his nose, I know as well as possible why he does it.'

'Lily Dale, you have no business to say so. It is not true. I don't know how you can bring yourself to talk in that way of your own clergyman. If I were to tell your mamma she would be shocked.'

'You won't be so ill-natured, Mrs Boyce, – after all that I've done for the church.'

'If you think more about the clergyman, Lily, and less about the church,' said Mrs Boyce very sententiously, 'more about the matter and less about the manner, more of the

reality and less of the form, I think you'd find that your religion would go further with you. Miss Crawley is the daughter of a clergyman, and I'm sure she'll agree with me.'

'If she agrees with anybody in scolding me I'll quarrel with her.'

'I didn't mean to scold you, Lily.'

'I don't mind it from you, Mrs Boyce. Indeed, I rather like it. It is a sort of pastoral visitation; and as Mr Boyce never scolds me himself I take it as coming from him by attorney.' Then there was silence for a minute or two, during which Mrs Boyce was endeavouring to discover whether Miss Dale was laughing at her or not. As she was not quite certain, she thought at last that she would let the suspected fault pass unobserved. 'Don't wait for us, Mrs Boyce,' said Lily. 'We must remain till Hopkins has sent Gregory to sweep the church out and take away the rubbish. We'll see that the key is left at Mrs Giles's.'

'Thank you, my dear. Then I may as well go. I thought I'd come in and see that it was all right. I'm sure Mr Boyce will be very much obliged to you and Miss Crawley. Good-night, my dear.'

'Good-night, Mrs Boyce; and be sure you don't let Mr Swanton be long to-morrow.' To this parting shot Mrs Boyce made no rejoinder; but she hurried out of the church somewhat the quicker for it, and closed the door after her with something of a slam.

Ghostly Encounters

WENDY BOASE

*Christmas hauntings are rare indeed, but one common
English legend is that of the mistletoe bough bride who, after
her wedding on Christmas Eve, hides herself in a wooden chest
during a game of hide and seek with her new husband.*

*According to the legend the groom is unable to find his bride,
she dies in her hiding place and subsequently haunts the house
where she met her untimely death.*

*In Hampshire it is Marwell Hall that our own version of
the mistletoe bough bride is said to haunt and, as the following
extract reveals, there is every reason to believe that Marwell
could actually be home to some ghostly bride or other.*

No legend of redemption, however, accompanies the tragic
tale of the death and subsequent haunting of the Mistletoe
Bough bride. This legend is traditionally associated with
Marwell Hall at Owslebury, though other houses such as
Bramshill at Eversley, now the Police Training College, also
claim the story. The wedding of the beautiful girl and the eli-
gible Lord Lovel took place on Christmas Eve and the man-
sion was decked with mistletoe and branches of holly. In playful mood, the bride challenged her husband to seek her out in
a hiding game. But though Lord Lovel and his friends
searched frantically for a week, they were unable to find her.

A Victorian song tells how, when Lord Lovel was an old man, his 'bride' was discovered:

> At length an oak chest that had long lain hid,
> Was found in the castle, they raised the lid,
> And a skeleton form lay mouldering there,
> In the bridal wreath of the lady fair.
> Oh! sad was her fate, in sportive jest
> She hid from her Lord, in the old oak chest,
> It closed with a spring, and her bridal bloom,
> Lay withering there, in a living tomb.
> Oh! the mistletoe bough!
> Oh! the mistletoe bough!

The chest has now vanished, but the ghost of the girl, dressed in her bridal garments, is said to haunt her former home.

Christmas hauntings – Scrooge is tormented by the spirits. From an early edition of *A Christmas Carol*

Marwell Hall is one of several places in England associated with this legend. But if the house proved not to be the true one, the presence of the ghostly bride might still be explained, for another and more famous wedding took place at Marwell. Here, while Anne Boleyn awaited execution in London, King Henry VIII married Jane Seymour. A year later Jane herself was dead and for long after haunted the corridors of the old house, so perhaps she is the spectral bride. Another apparition which still walks down an avenue of yew trees in the garden is thought by some to be that of Anne Boleyn, who has returned to bring misfortune on the home of her successor. As the house has long passed from the Seymour family, and Anne Boleyn's ghost frequents other places with better cause, it seems unlikely that this 'White Lady' can be her.

Squoyling

GILBERT SMITH

Whether you agree with it or not there is no getting away from the fact that hunting has always been an integral part of New Forest life.

'Squoyling', an ancient custom which involved tracking down squirrels on either Boxing Day or New Year's day, represents perhaps one of the more barbaric types of hunt to take place in the Forest.

The word 'squoyle' refers not to the squirrel, but to the short stick, weighted at one end, which was thrown at the animals as they ran from branch to branch.

It is perhaps worth reminding ourselves that this custom was more than mere sport. It provided a good meal for Forest folk in the days after Christmas and was also used to control the squirrel population.

The following two extracts, the first written in 1904 and the second, from the memoirs of New Forest keeper Gilbert Smith, written as recently as 1984, illustrate how widespread this custom was.

The only right, if it is so to be called, that the people seem to enjoy quite freely and without any restriction at all, is that of 'squoyling' at the squirrels. For them there seems to be no close time whatever. And yet the 'squoyling' does not seem to be done to any such extent as to diminish the squirrels' numbers at all. They flourish, fully as much as is good for the young timber, in spite of it. The truth is, that the 'squoyling' is not pursued very persistently. New Year's day is the great time for it, and at other holiday seasons parties may be made up for 'squoyling' competitions, to see who will come home with the biggest bag. But the squirrel increases and multiplies, notwithstanding that the forest folk enjoy many a squirrel pie.

It is impossible not to perceive how greatly these rights and pursuits of the people must have been extended by the increased opportunities given by the removal of the deer, probably the most salutary measure ever passed in the interests of the children of the New Forest.

We looked forward to Boxing Days to go squirrelling. Not after the grey tree rats we see in the New Forest today, but

that gorgeous creature that we see here no more, the red squirrel. The red squirrel could never be described as vermin but their numbers had to be controlled, otherwise the young bucks in June would tear about the trees, particularly the larch, and rind the top with the result that the tree died. We went after the squirrels armed with snogs – lethal weapons made from pieces of wood with a lead weight wired on the end. These would be used to knock the squirrels from the trees and when we had about a dozen we would take them home to be skinned and cooked in the turf oven. They made a very tasty meal.

Christmas 1924

THOMAS HARDY

Grim though it is I felt I had to include the following four-line verse from the pen of Thomas Hardy.

Surely no one but the great Wessex writer himself could have come up with such a bitterly ironic statement in the space of so few words – and at Christmas too!

'Peace on earth!' was said. We sing it,
And pay a million priests to bring it.
After two thousand years of mass
We've got as far as poison-gas.

'Hark! The Herald Angels Sing'

CHARLES WESLEY

'Hark! The Herald Angels Sing' has to be one of the most popular carols ever written. In fact it took Charles Wesley less than an hour to compose this Christmas classic, as he walked across the fields to church on the Christmas morning of 1735. Wesley was the younger brother of John, who preached at Portsmouth in what is now known as the Unitarian Chapel.

Hark! The herald angels sing
Glory to the new born king,
Peace on earth, and mercy mild,
God and sinners reconciled.
Joyful, all ye nations, rise,
Join the triumph of the skies;
With the angelic host proclaim:
'Christ is born in Bethlehem'.
Hark! The herald angels sing
Glory to the new-born King.

Christ, by highest Heaven adored
Christ, the everlasting Lord,

Late in time behold him come,
Offspring of a virgin's womb.
Veiled in flesh the Godhead see!
Hail, the incarnate Deity!
Pleased as man with man to dwell,
Jesus, our Immanuel:
Hark! The herald angels sing
Glory to the new-born King.

Hail, the heaven born Prince of Peace!
Hail, the Son of Righteousness!
Light and life to all he brings,
Risen with healing in his wings.
Mild he lays his glory by,
Born that man no more may die,
Born to raise the sons of Earth,
Born to give them second birth:
Hark! The herald angels sing
Glory to the new-born King.

from

A Christmas Carol

CHARLES DICKENS

Since it was written in 1843 the conversion of the anti-social miser Scrooge into a charitable fellow, thoroughly dedicated to Christmas cheer, has become one of the best-loved legends of Christmas.

In his preface to the first edition Dickens declared 'I have endeavoured in this Ghostly little book to raise the Ghost of an Idea which shall not put my readers out of humour with themselves, with each other, with the season or with me. May it haunt their house pleasantly and no one wish to lay it.'

As I began this collection with the miserly Scrooge it is only appropriate that I end with the reformed Scrooge, intended by Hampshire-born Charles Dickens to be a lesson to everyone who scoffs at Christmas.

He went to church, and walked about the streets, and watched the people hurrying to and fro, and patted children on the head, and questioned beggars, and looked down into the kitchens of houses, and up to the windows, and found that everything could yield him pleasure. He had never dreamed

that any walk – that anything – could give him so much happiness. In the afternoon he turned his steps towards his nephew's house.

He passed the door a dozen times, before he had the courage to go up and knock. But he made a dash, and did it.

'Is your master at home, my dear?' said Scrooge to the girl. Nice girl! Very.

'Yes, sir.'

'Where is he, my love?' said Scrooge.

'He's in the dining-room, sir, along with mistress. I'll show you up-stairs, if you please.'

'Thank'ee. He knows me,' said Scrooge with his hand already on the dining-room lock. 'I'll go in here, my dear.'

He turned it gently, and sidled his face in, round the door. They were looking at the table (which was spread out in great array); for these young housekeepers are always nervous on such points, and like to see that everything is right.

'Fred!' said Scrooge.

Dear heart alive, how his niece by marriage started! Scrooge had forgotten, for the moment, about her sitting in the corner with the footstool, or he wouldn't have done it, on any account.

'Why bless my soul!' cried Fred, 'who's that?'

'It's I. Your uncle Scrooge. I have come to dinner. Will you let me in, Fred?'

Let him in! It is a mercy he didn't shake his arm off. He was at home in five minutes. Nothing could be heartier. His niece looked just the same. So did Topper when *he* came. So did the plump sister when *she* came. So did every one when *they* came. Wonderful party, wonderful games, wonderful unanimity, won-der-ful happiness!

But he was early at the office next morning. Oh, he was early there. If he could only be there first, and catch Bob Cratchit coming late! That was the thing he had set his heart upon.

Preface.

I have endeavoured in this Ghostly little book, to raise the Ghost of an Idea, which shall not put my readers out of humour with themselves, with each other, with the Season, or with me. May it haunt their houses pleasantly and no one wish to lay it!

Their faithful friend and Servant

CD.

December 1843

Dickens' preface to *A Christmas Carol*

And he did it; yes, he did! The clock struck nine. No Bob. A quarter past. No Bob. He was full eighteen minutes and a half behind his time. Scrooge sat with this door wide open, that he might see him come into the Tank.

His hat was off, before he opened the door; his comforter too. He was on his stool in a jiffy; driving away with his pen, as if he were trying to overtake nine o'clock.

'Hallo!' growled Scrooge, in his accustomed voice, as near as he could feign it. 'What do you mean by coming here at this time of day?'

'I am very sorry, sir,' said Bob. 'I *am* behind my time.'

'You are?' repeated Scrooge. 'Yes. I think you are. Step this way, sir, if you please.'

'It's only once a year, sir,' pleaded Bob, appearing from the Tank. 'It shall not be repeated. I was making rather merry yesterday, sir.'

'Now, I'll tell you what, my friend,' said Scrooge, 'I am not going to stand this sort of thing any longer. And therefore,' he continued, leaping from his stool, and giving Bob such a dig

in the waistcoat that he staggered back into the Tank again; 'and therefore I am about to raise your salary!'

Bob trembled, and got a little nearer to the ruler. He had a momentary idea of knocking Scrooge down with it, holding him, and calling to the people in the court for help and a strait-waistcoat.

'A merry Christmas, Bob!' said Scrooge, with an earnestness that could not be mistaken, as he clapped him on the back. 'A merrier Christmas, Bob, my good fellow, than I have given you for many a year! I'll raise your salary, and endeavour to assist your struggling family, and we will discuss your affairs this very afternoon, over a Christmas bowl of smoking bishop, Bob! Make up the fires, and buy another coal-skuttle before you dot another i, Bob Cratchit!'

Scrooge was better than his word. He did it all, and infinitely more; and to Tiny Tim, who did NOT die, he was a second father. He became as good a friend, as good a master, and as good a man, as the good old city knew, or any other good old city, town, or borough, in the good old world. Some people laughed to see the alteration in him, but he let them laugh, and little heeded them; for he was wise enough to know that nothing ever happened on this globe, for good, at which some people did not have their fill of laughter in the outset; and knowing that such as these would be blind anyway, he thought it quite as well that they should wrinkle up their eyes in grins, as have the malady in less attractive forms. His own heart laughed; and that was quite enough for him.

He had no further intercourse with Spirits, but lived upon the Total Abstinence Principle, ever afterwards; and it was always said of him, that he knew how to keep Christmas well, if any man alive possessed the knowledge. May that be truly said of us, and all of us! And so, as Tiny Tim observed, God bless Us, Every One!

Acknowledgements

A Hampshire Christmas' by John Arlott was first published in *Hampshire – the county magazine,* December 1966 and is reprinted by permission of Paul Cave Publications Ltd. *Nothing to steal* by Nancy Sharman was first published in 1977 and is reprinted by permission of Kaye and Ward. 'Some Ghosts of Christmas Past' by Joan Grigsby was first published in *Hampshire – the county magazine,* December 1974 and is reprinted by permission of Paul Cave Publications Ltd. 'Food Glorious Food' by Irene Soper was first published in *New Forest Cookery* by Arcady Books (1984) and is reprinted by permission of Rose Cottage Books. 'Christmastide' by Thomas Hardy was first published in *Winter Words* (1928). *My Old Chap* by Norman Goodland was first published in 1978 and is reprinted by permission of the author.'Hogmanay in Hampshire' by C.W. Hawkins was first published in *The Story of Alton* (1973) by Alton District Council and is reprinted by permission of the author's son, Mr C. Hawkins. 'God Bless Us, Every One' by Charles Clark was first published in *Hampshire – the county magazine,* December 1979 and is reprinted by permission of Paul Cave Publications Ltd. *Sandy Balls for all Seasons* was first published in 1977 and is reprinted by permission of the author and Sandy Balls Press. *Old Men Remember Life on Victoria's Smaller Island* was first published in 1988 by the Ventnor and District Local History Society and is reprinted by permission of the Society. *Memories of Bitterne* by Irene Pilson was first published in 1984 and is reprinted by permission of the author. 'Carolling' by Norman Goodland was first published in *Village Green* (1988) and is reprinted by permission of the author and Paul Cave Publications Ltd. 'Old Palace House Festivities' by E.A. Mitchell was first published in the *Southern Daily Echo* (December 1938) and is reprinted by permission

of *Southern Newspapers.* 'The Mummer's Play' was first published in *It Happened in Hampshire* by Winnifred G. Beddington and Elsa B. Christy (1936) and is reprinted by permission of The Hampshire Federation of Women's Institutes. *An Old Woman's Outlook* by Charlotte Yonge was first published in 1892 by Macmillan. 'The Oxen' by Thomas Hardy was first published in *The Times,* 24 December 1915. 'Old Christmas Eve' by Bert Butler was first published in *Hampshire and Wessex Life* (1974). 'Christmas Tree Poaching'. The first extract by Norman Goodland was published in *Morning Stories* (1984) and is reprinted by permission of the author and Paul Cave Publications Ltd. The second extract by Gilbert Smith was published in *Man of the Forest* (1984) and is reprinted by permission of Paul Cave Publications Ltd. *A New Forest Commoner Remembers* by Hugh Pasmore was first published in 1991 by New Forest Leaves and is reprinted by permission of New Forest Leaves. 'Ghostly Encounters' by Wendy Boase was first published in *Folklore of Hampshire and the Isle of Wight* (1976) and is reprinted by permission of Batsford Press. 'Squoyling'. The first extract was published in *The New Forest* by Horace G. Hutchinson (1904). The second extract was published in *Man of the Forest* (1984) and is reprinted by permission of Paul Cave Publications Ltd. 'Christmas 1924' by Thomas Hardy was first published in *Winter Words* (1928).

Picture Credits

From *A Christmas Carol* by Charles Dickens. A Facsimile Reproduction of the Author's Original Manuscript (1890), p. 149; from *Charles Dickens by Pen and Pencil* by Frederick C. Kitton (1890), p.5; Hampshire County Libraries, pp. 19, 56; *Southern Newspapers*, pp. 3, 8, 13, 21, 25, 33, 39, 40, 55, 64, 66, 68, 72, 81, 82, 114, 121, 126, 130; from *The Works of Charles Dickens in 21 volumes,* vol. IV (1901), pp. 141, 150.